HANS ANDERSEN

Son of Denmark

E·P·DUTTON & CO.INC.
1852 1952
CELEBRATING 100 YEARS OF PUBLISHING

HANS ANDERSEN

SON OF DENMARK

by

OPAL WHEELER

ILLUSTRATED BY

HENRY C. PITZ

E. P. DUTTON & CO., INC. NEW YORK

First Printing September 1951
Second Printing August 1952

For

Belva

HANS ANDERSEN

Son of Denmark

CHAPTER ONE

SPRING had just come to little Denmark, and the early sun was fast driving the curling mist from the tiny island of Fyn. Soon, now, the Easter processions would begin. Clippity-clop, clippity-clop! Wooden shoes beat fast on the wet cobbles of Odense as neighbors hurried to finish their chores in time.

Young Hans Christian hung from the doorway of his one-room home, bright blue eyes watching splashing water buckets and strings of fresh fish dangling from stout Danish shoulders.

"'Morning, Miss Claus! 'Morning, Miss Collin!" his clear little voice piped gently through the fog.

Village faces warmed into smiles as they turned to the shadowy little figure.

"And a right fair day to you, small yellow head!" made him chuckle happily.

From the low-roofed cottage behind him came the steady tap, tap, tap of a hammer. Hans's lean fingers beat an accompaniment on the sagging door, while he fashioned a delicate sweet melody that was finished almost as soon as it had begun.

"Parades coming now, For?" his shock of bright hair jerked backward.

Hammer sounds were no answer, and in a flash the thin little body was pressed against the cobbler's side. Big Hans let his tools fall to the bench with a clatter.

"So many times the same asking, little one." The tired eyes found new life in the brighter blue ones, close to his own.

"And Mor will be here in time?" The four-year-old climbed onto the slender knees and buried his head on his father's shoulder.

"Your mother should be through the washing by now," was the patient reply. "But food there must be for growing boys, and a good thing the big house has need of fresh clothes."

Hans felt a warm cheek rest lightly on his scraggly locks.

"Tell me tales, For."

Big Hans sighed and gently stroked the long, thin legs of the child who meant more to him than life itself.

"Ah well, tales are better than cobbling," said he. "Now this very morning, little rabbit, I could not help thinking of the day you were born," he began. "Your wailing cut into the very chinks of this old room, and not a single word of my songs or beautiful plays did you hear."

Small Hans's silvery laughter rang through the cottage.

"And For, you said, 'Wilt thou go to sleep, or listen quietly?' And I did not go to sleep."

Big Hans smiled. "And you did not stop your wailing, even to the day you were baptized. At the terrible din, the preacher clapped his hands to his ears. 'The young one screams like a cat!' he shouted."

Small Hans never let the tale end there.

"But Godfather Gomar said, 'No matter. The louder he cries, the better he will sing as he grows older.'"

Hans sat up suddenly, head cocked on one side.

"Trumpets! Parades are coming, For."

He was out of the door just as the sun broke through the clouds, arms and legs churning the air as he sped over the worn cobbles.

There, rounding the corner was the procession, three horn players and a dancing clown in bright red. Hans gazed in awe at the fat scrubbed ox lumbering behind, his horns decked with branches and flowers. On his back sat a fair young angel in snowy garments, long paper wings floating from his shoulders.

Hans Christian's breath came jerkily as he watched the fine spectacle. The next minute he was in the parade, dancing as fast as his wooden shoes would allow.

"See the Andersen boy!" laughed the neighbors from their doorways. "What long arms and legs he has. Poor mite! Looks as though he never knew a full meal."

Now all the children in the neighborhood had joined the procession and Hans slipped behind the clown, following his every movement. Leaping, turning, and bowing, he blew handfuls of kisses to the shouting crowd.

In a burst of joy he danced over the cobbles and when he came to his house, cried out with all his might.

"For! Mor! Look—I'm in the parade!"

But no one answered his calls. A faint tapping told him that not even the Easter procession had taken his father from his workbench.

At the river's edge the parade came to an end. His face still aglow, Hans turned back to his street, humming the tune of the trumpeters. Suddenly a terrible sound struck his ears.

"Crazy man! Crazy man! Ha! Ha! Ha!"

Darting into an alleyway, he crouched against the wall, his breath coming in short, sharp sobs.

The jeering crowd was coming closer now, and Hans could not help seeing the dreadful sight from his hiding place. Shouting and laughing and tapping their heads with their fingers, the neighbor boys danced round an old man.

But the bent little creature did not seem to mind. Smiling and waving his basket over his head, he skipped about, giving away the last animals that he had worked so long to carve.

The noisy throng edged on down the street and Hans crept trembling from his hiding place. Like a deer he bounded home, and throwing himself on the big bed in the corner, wept as though his heart would break.

His mother, just home from the washing, hurried to him, comforting him with roughened hands.

"Come, little one, what has hurt you so sorely?" she asked gently.

The words came out in a fresh burst of sobbing.

"It was grandfather—and the boys—and the names."

Big Hans bowed his head and his hammer was silent. Ane Marie did not look at him, as lightly she patted the small shoulders.

"Never mind, child. The words do not harm your grandfather. He does not even hear them. He thinks of things we do not know about, and is quite happy in his own way."

When the weeping did not stop, she said, as if to herself, "I wonder if anything is happening in my garden."

The words were magic. At once the scraggly yellow head was raised from the bed. Scrambling to his feet, Hans wiped his face with his sleeve.

"I'll go see, Mor!"

Climbing the tiny ladder to the roof, he ran over the red tiles to the big chest of dirt in the gutter. His long, thin nose wrinkled happily at the fresh spring smells, and scrambling on all fours to the ladder opening, he shouted below.

"Eighteen green shoots, Mor! Garden coming fine!"

It was fun up there under the sky, and his troubles forgotten, Hans lay on his back, dreaming of sailing away on the puffball clouds. Far, far out into the world he drifted on a scarlet carpet to seek bags of gold. And never would they be poor again.

"Soup, Hans!" called his mother. His long legs found the steep ladder steps, to be swallowed up in the darkness below.

"And real holiday soup, at that!" declared Ane Marie as she ladeled out the steaming broth at the tiny stove. "Peddler going home, vegetables all sold, when I spied leavings on the floor of his cart—half a cabbage, some turnips, a few potatoes, and carrots."

She stopped a moment, a half smile lighting her weary face.

" 'No good to anyone,' said I to the man. 'Half an ore for the lot.' And before I knew it, they were in my apron."

Her husband put down a half-soled shoe.

"Smart old woman," said he, nodding wisely.

"Smart woman," echoed small Hans, and seated himself at the rough boards.

Pleased at their words, Ane Marie cut larger chunks of black bread than usual, and piled them in the middle of the table.

Just as the feast was ending, a shadow fell over the doorsill and a cheery voice startled the little family.

"Bestimor!" shouted Hans, racing to the worn old figure, to be caught in his grandmother's arms in a warm hug.

"Sit in with us for soup, there's still aplenty," invited her son.

"Ah, no. Too little time, with so much raking and burning at the poorhouse gardens. I just stopped in to see if a small boy might like to help me."

With a shout of joy, Hans slipped into his patched coat and the two were on their way. Soon they were hard at work, cleaning the grounds after the long winter months.

There was much to be done, to be ready for the seed planting, and Hans ran about in his old shoes, piling up dead leaves and branches. And how he laughed and shouted for joy when the great heap was set afire.

"The world's burning up, Bestimor!" he cried, his face alight from the dancing flames.

When the last spark was out, he followed his grandmother into the large building for food. Always it was a feast, and

Hans hummed happily as he munched away on fish and meal cakes.

"The spinning room, Bestimor," he begged, finishing the last crumb on the crude plate. "They will be waiting for me in there."

His grandmother watched with pride as he stood before the poor old women at their looms. With a piece of chalk he was making rapid strokes on the door as his father had done at home.

"Today, ladies, I will show you your insides," he explained, his arm sweeping in air.

Big circles sprawled on the rough boards and Hans's voice rose in excitement.

"There is your heart, and lung, and down below, your intestines. See—you are filled, filled with them!" Twisting, turning lines ran in all directions.

The simple-minded women watched in awe.

"Tsch! Tsch! Tsch! Such a clever boy!" they clucked. "Too bright to live long."

But better than drawing and singing and reciting for the poor folk, Hans liked to listen to their tales. He lay on the floor at their feet, drinking in their stories. And filled with witches and goblins and black magic they were. Horror grew with each tale until poor Hans shook with fright. Scrambling to his feet, he ran home as fast as he could go and hid, trembling, behind the long curtains of the big bed.

"Tales, only tales," said his father quietly, watching two large blue eyes staring out through the opening.

Ane Marie put down her mending at once.

"Time for us all to be sleeping," said she. "Up with you, son, and into your own crib."

With a loud scraping noise the smaller bed was pulled from under the larger. There was nothing to do now but to go to bed, with not an inch of space left to turn around in. Wicks were blown out, and soon all was quiet for the night in the simple cottage of Cobbler Andersen.

Sunday morning dawned clear and still and Hans tumbled from the snowy linen sheets.

"Mor! For!" he called. "It's holiday. Time to go to the woods."

This was the best day of all the week and very special, now that April had come. Not only his father, but Ane Marie, would go to the woods with him.

Hans sang for joy as his mother put on her one holiday dress of flowered calico, and made herself ready for her yearly visit to the beeches.

After bowls of coarse meal porridge, the little family set out, and arriving at the edge of the village, prepared to enjoy themselves for the day.

Ane Marie busied herself at once, gathering great armloads of fresh green branches. Small Hans raced here and there like a wild rabbit, exploring hidden glades and shallow caves, or lay as still as a mouse as birds built their nests over his head. Then, in a burst of joy, he sang his heart out while he made garlands of leaves and early spring blossoms.

Bread and cheese never tasted so good as under the leafy green trees, the sun dappling the mossy earth with coins of gold as the little family sat together.

Ane Marie and big Hans watched with loving care as glowing color crept into the white cheeks of the boy who was fast outgrowing his patched clothing.

"Read me tales, For."

From his pocket, his father drew a precious worn copy of Arabian Nights. Shivering with delight, Hans hugged his knees under his chin, to listen hungrily until the shadows grew long and twittering birds told of early nightfall.

"Here is your share for carrying, son." Ane Marie stopped the story with filling the boy's arms with sweet-smelling boughs.

Overladen, the three trooped contentedly back through the quiet Odense streets to the little cottage. And what a happy time there was, trimming the room.

"The big bed, Mor—we'll make it look like trees in the wood!" Up the posts scrambled Hans, thrusting the tender green shoots over the curtains.

At last every nook and cranny was decorated and he looked around him with eager, shining eyes, sniffing the spring-

scented room that seemed almost like heaven to him now.

How he loved his simple home, so neat and clean, with crude pictures by his father scrawled over the walls and doors. Copper pots and kettles gleamed in the firelight at his side, where his mother was busying herself with soup for her hungry family.

Now would come the hours that he loved more than anything else in all the world. At the very thought, he sang with delight, and fell upon his supper with such haste as to make his mother cry out with vexation.

"Is the soup so poor that you must be rid of it in such a hurry?"

Hans hung his head for shame and a low, "I'm sorry, Mor," made things right again.

The longed-for moment arrived at last. His eager hands found the small puppet theater under the bed and put it carefully on the table.

"Ah yes, yes," murmured his father, looking over the characters one by one. "The king's right shoe needs a bit of mending. My needle, son."

In a few moments all was in readiness. Ane Marie, busy with her mending, smiled as she listened to the voices, now laughing, weeping, shouting angrily, or sighing, as big hands and little hands worked the strings of the tiny puppet dolls in one play after another.

"Next time I will be the beggar, For," announced Hans as the theater was carefully packed away for the night.

"And we will need a new princess before then," answered

his father. "Perhaps you could try your hand in making her. But now, a chapter from the Holy Book, before sleep."

The cobbler found the place while Hans crawled onto the big bed to listen, sleepy-eyed, to the flowing sounds. And so beautiful they were when his father read them, that Ane Marie put down her sewing to enjoy them.

The last thing that Hans remembered, was the quiet prayer after the reading. "Thank Thee, Lord, for this day. Keep our hearts clean and pure. Amen."

With the days, the sun grew warmer, and in the tiny front yard, Hans stretched his mother's apron between the wall and the currant bush which he, himself, had planted with such care. For hours he sat under his home-made tent, watching through half-closed eyes the sunlight playing on the leaves.

In his mind, fairies and princesses and witches flew here and there, lighting on the branches and speaking with him in their own language.

Rocking back and forth, Hans hugged his knees in purest joy one morning, when his father's voice broke in on his dreaming.

"Come in, come in, sir! And what can I do for you, sir?"

There in the doorway stood a young boy, a strapful of books dangling from his shoulder. He must be from the manor house, to bring so many 'sirs' from the cobbler. Hans crept nearer to listen.

"Father says I am to have new boots," explained the customer. "Of your finest leather, please."

"To be sure, sir," agreed the shoemaker, carefully measuring the bared foot. But all the while he glanced hungrily at the dangling books. "Tell me, young sir, how do you like studying at school? Now I don't suppose you read from all those volumes in one day?" his words rushed on eagerly.

The boy listened in surprise. No one had ever cared about his studies before. Opening the books carelessly, he explained briefly, the cobbler hanging on every word.

When he had gone, big Hans strode after him to the low doorway to watch him go down the street. Suddenly he reached out his arms, clasping young Hans to him tightly.

"Did you hear, boy?" he cried. "The young man is a gentleman! He reads and studies from books!"

Hans looked up at his father to see tears glistening in his eyes as the words poured from his lips.

"All my life long I wanted to learn from books. Every day as a boy I dreamed of going to school. But when the time came, evils flocked around us like crows. The cattle died of a strange sickness and one black night the farmhouse burned to the ground and poor Father lost his senses. Little Mother led us both to town, and sent me to learn the trade of a cobbler."

He stopped suddenly, his eyes on Ane Marie, who was about to leave for her day's work.

"Our son will never follow the trade of a cobbler," he declared slowly. "Make him ready, wife. It is time he started to school."

At his father's words, Hans cried out in alarm.

"No, no! The big one carries a stick. She will beat me!" he wailed miserably.

Ane Marie turned to him quickly, her voice sharp.

"Mark you, Hans Christian—there will be no beatings. No son of mine will ever feel a teacher's rod!"

The very next morning the two set out for school, Hans's yellow hair washed and curled and his patched clothing neat and clean.

"No beatings, Mor?" he kept asking, trying to keep up with his mother's long strides.

"No beatings," was the stern answer.

Hans looked in awe at the sea of young faces in the crowded schoolroom as he took his place on the hard bench. His hands clenched suddenly as he saw the long rod behind the high-backed chair. "No beatings!" he whispered to himself, and sat up, electrified, as a loud voice rasped in his ears.

"Man!" shouted the teacher, her long bony fingers pointing to the children.

With one accord they leaped to their feet, screaming out the letters. But the teacher was not satisfied.

"So quiet you are today. Come now, much louder, and in a higher key: RAT!"

Poor Hans tried to keep up with the rest, screaming until he was hoarse and his thin legs were weary with standing. Then, how still the room seemed when the voices were quiet! In the silence, the loveliest thread of sound stole gently to his ears.

The tiny doors of the tall clock behind the teacher's chair opened on the hour. Little figures in quaint costume marched around in a circle to the tinkling of bells and disappeared with the closing portals.

It was time to go home, and his eyes alight, Hans raced back to the cottage.

"You learned much in the school today, my son?" His father sprang to meet him as soon as the door opened.

His head on one side, Hans looked up at him.

"Oh For, the bells in the clock made a little tune that goes like this," he cried, and sang the delicate melody.

"There was nothing more?" the cobbler's voice was quiet.

"No, For—only screaming."

One morning, not long afterward, weary with shouting numbers and spelling, Hans sat down on the hard bench. Sighing, he drifted off in a world of his own, waiting for the little figures to march around the clock. He would make puppet men just like them for his theater.

Smiling at the thought, he went on with his planning, when

a sudden gasp from the children made him look up quickly. There, just over his head was the long black stick. Whack! Down came the rod with a sickening blow across his knuckles.

"That will teach you to listen, young dreamer!" shouted an angry voice in his ears.

With a scream of pain, Hans shot from the room and ran headlong down the street, holding tightly the aching, stinging hand. Neighbors, hearing his cries, hurried to their doorways.

"Something terrible has happened to the Andersen boy!"

His shouts did not stop as he burst sobbing into the cottage.

"She beat me, For! The tall one beat me!"

Big Hans fell to his knees beside the trembling figure, wiping away the tears and binding up the swollen fingers.

"You shall never see her again," he comforted. "There are other and better schools in Odense."

It was not long before Ane Marie put on her brown calico dress and led her son to the Carsten's school for boys. There was no rod to be seen, and Hans Christian sighed with relief as he sat next to the only girl in the room.

"I am going to be a dairymaid some day," she whispered proudly, smiling at the new boy.

Hans's eyelids flickered a moment.

"Then you may work in my castle, where I shall be a nobleman," he answered seriously.

His seatmate laughed aloud.

"Why, you are only a poor boy!" she declared haughtily.

Taking out his treasured pencil, Hans's fingers flew over the paper, turrets and towers of a fine castle rising over a hill.

"This was once my home," he explained in low tones. "But one night, in the shadow of the moon, I was stolen away and given to a poor couple here in Odense, to bring up as their son. And now," he whispered, his blue eyes half closing as his tale grew, "each night the angels of God fly to my bedside to speak with me."

But the girl only laughed the more. Turning to the older boys she cried, "You should hear what Hans has been telling me! He is only a fool, like his grandfather."

The words cut into his heart like a whip. How glad he was when the director looked at him from his desk, smiling.

"Come, Andersen, a little air will do us all good," said he, holding out his hand to his youngest pupil.

The master was kind, indeed, protecting him from the older boys in their rough games and going over and over the lessons with endless patience. Quickly he came to love the shy young Hans, bringing him sweetmeats and flowers. And repaid a thousandfold he was by the smile that sprang to the white little face like a burst of sunshine.

"The boy is different," he explained to his helper. "Something is here that I do not yet understand. He learns his lessons simply by hearing them, and lives in a fairy world all his own. With a heart so beautiful, he will suffer much, I fear."

Big Hans was delighted in the change in his son, and listened to his lessons with pride.

"God willing, our son will be a gentleman some day, with all his learning," he would declare proudly.

One morning, Hans Christian arrived at school later than usual, his one suit just washed and mended by Ane Marie. As he took his place at the table with the others, he was startled at seeing an older boy standing with book in hand in the center of the table.

"Pay him no attention," cautioned the master. "He does not know his lessons and must be punished for his forgetful ways."

But Hans could not take his eyes from the shamed red face above him, and when he could stand it no longer, put his head down on his arms, sobbing out his grief.

"Come, come Andersen!" Carsten was bending over him. "Are you in pain, young one?"

"Yes sir, in here," said Hans, pointing to his breast. "Because the forgetful one is hurting so, inside."

"Aha!" laughed the master. "That is easily mended for both of you. Down, forgetful one! And better lessons tomorrow, yes?"

Fall and harvesting time came to the farmers on the edge of Odense, and Ane Marie was happy. Now she could earn a few extra coins gleaning in the fields.

"School does not keep today, and you may come with me, Hans Christian," she announced one morning. "Your hands will be of help, at least until noontide."

Hans was delighted and was soon treading the stubbly open meadows with the group of neighbor women, picking up stray pieces of grain left behind the reapers.

But the sun was hot and the sweet-smelling fields made him drowsy. Stretching out under a bush, he looked up through the bright yellow leaves, his breath coming fast at the glory of gold against the blue sky.

A meadowlark, startled from her resting place, whirred upward with song of such beauty that Hans sprang to his feet. His heart pounded as he watched the circling creature mount higher and higher, the joyous lilting sounds swinging gently back to him.

Suddenly a cry rang out over the fields.

"Hans! Hans!" Ane Marie's frightened calls brought him her warning. "The bailiff is coming! Run for the roadway!"

There at the edge of the meadow a tall heavy man was striding, a long black whip swinging from his hand. He would teach these women to work faster!

Fear clutching at his heart, Hans started to run as fast as his legs would carry him, when his wooden shoes caught in the brambles. Leaving them behind, he darted on, but the thistles cut deeply into the bare flesh and he stopped short, gasping with pain.

The overseer was close now and Hans trembled with terror. Dread tales he had heard of the harsh ruler of the farmlands, and he waited for the punishment that was sure to come swiftly.

"So!" growled the hoarse voice at his shoulder. "They have left you to the mercy of the bailiff!"

Suddenly Hans wheeled to face the big man with whip raised over his head.

"How dare you strike, when God can see you?" he cried out with all his might.

Slowly the whip dropped and the big man laughed heartily.

"Such a little head for a big thought!" he roared, slapping his hip with the leather thong. "Who are you, boy, and what are you doing here?"

Hans's breath came more evenly now, and fear began to leave his eyes.

"I am only Hans Andersen, and I help my mother because we are very poor—but respectable."

The big man laughed again, and putting coins in the small hand, found the shoes and slipped them on the boy's feet.

"You are a good lad. Off with you now," said the bailiff, going back the way he had come.

Ane Marie and the women stood watching, speechless with astonishment.

"See—the harsh one has filled his fist with money!" exclaimed his mother, taking the coins and putting them carefully in her pocket. "The lad has a strange power. Everyone is so kind to him."

And now a new character was added to the puppet theater, and big Hans smiled as he watched the wicked bailiff stalking over the field, roaring and blustering and cracking his whip. Young Hans's voice filled the cottage with his fury as he worked the strings of the doll he had labored so hard to make.

"My son," said his father, when the act came to an end, "how would you like to go to a real theater and see a real play?"

Hans could not believe his ears.

"Real people acting on a real stage, For?" he cried.

"Yes. Your mother will make you ready, and in two days we will go."

Such excitement as there was in the one-room cottage, with special hair washing and curling on rags. His father's clothes, just cut down for him, were put on with great care.

"Now for the finishing touches, Hans." Ane Marie sighed proudly as she carefully pinned four large pieces of checkered silk across the small breast. With a bright kerchief tied in a mighty bow around his neck, he was ready in all his finery.

Hearts beating high with joy, the little family set out. Arriving at the theater, Hans's blue eyes opened wide at the large number of citizens gathered together.

"Mor! For!" he cried, his arm sweeping in a circle. "If we only had as many casks of butter as all these people, then I would eat lots of butter!"

Never would he forget his first beautiful play, and every

day from then on, as soon as his lessons were at an end, Hans's long legs led him straight to the theater.

"My best customer," laughed the man at the door, handing him a program. "See that you make a good play this time!"

Crawling into a corner of the old building, Hans Christian eagerly read the names of the people who would take part in the next performance. In a moment he would forget everything around him, and half closing his eyes, made a whole play in his mind for the characters to act out.

Darkness had fallen one evening just as he finished, and numb with the cold, he roused himself. Beating his hands to warm them, he ran home over the cobbles to find his father talking in a loud voice.

"New hope for us all!" he exclaimed, his eyes alight. "A shoemaker is needed at the big manor house in the next village. And the lucky man will have a fine house to live in, free, with a cow and a patch of land to till!"

Young Hans could hardly believe the news.

"And I could milk the cow and raise the biggest vegetables on the whole island of Fyn!" he cried, his face aglow.

Big Hans took from his pocket a piece of fine silk and laid it carefully on the bench.

"'Make for me a pair of shoes that will be the pride of the land, my good Andersen,' said the mistress to me. 'And if they prove worthy, you will be manor cobbler the rest of your days.'"

The very next morning the task was begun and Hans hung over the workbench, watching with bated breath as the shoes took form. Never did his father work so hard and never did so many fine stitches go into a pair of boots. And not a single evening did Hans forget to say his prayer: "Please, God, make Father the manor shoemaker."

At last the boots were finished and Hans danced about in a frenzy of joy as neighbors from miles around came to admire the handiwork.

"The house is as good as yours, Cobbler," they declared. "But we will miss you sorely after you have left this old cottage."

With pride big Hans wrapped the shoes in a spotless handkerchief, and Ane Marie and young Hans waved him into the sunny street as he trod the rough cobbles toward the manor house.

The hours went slowly by and at every footstep, Hans ran to the door.

"Patience, my son," said his mother. "It will take time to talk over the new home and the many duties your father will have at the manor house."

But when nightfall came and still he had not arrived, Ane Marie was alarmed, indeed. Throwing a shawl around her shoulders, she was about to set out with Hans at her side, when a long shadow darkened the doorway.

In strode the cobbler, his face clouded with anger.

"She would not have the shoes!" he cried. "She said that I had spoiled the silk!"

Hans stood rooted to the spot. No new home in the country. No garden to tend. He felt an arm tighten suddenly around his small shoulders and heard his father's words pouring into his ear.

"You will be proud of me yet, my son. I shall go off with the army, and come back a lieutenant, with ribbons aplenty flying from my breast. Then away to the country we will go for a fine holiday, you, and your mother and I."

And off as a soldier he went. Young Hans, in bed with the measles, listened with tears and beating heart to the drums outside, and the marching of feet. A cheery voice from the doorway startled him from his misery.

"My measly little boy, here all by himself!" Bestimor came to the crude bed, feeling the hot forehead of her eight-year-old grandson. "I must search at once for a chicken wing, a hawk's beak and mouse's tail to bind on the chest. 'Tis an excellent cure for childish ills, I am told."

The days seemed endless, and the cottage no longer rang with the tapping of the cobbler's hammer. His dearest friend and comrade was gone from the bench by the snowy-curtained window, and Hans was lonelier than he had ever been.

Ane Marie worked harder than ever at her washing, to earn a living without the help of her husband. And happily, Hans ran errands for the neighbors, bringing his hard-earned ore to his mother each evening. But best of all, there were ends of velvet ribbons and scraps of silk from the milliner to clothe his puppets. Faster and faster flew his needle in the candle-light. There must be plenty of new characters for the plays running through his mind, to surprise Father Andersen when he returned.

And then one evening, the quiet was broken by the sound of footsteps on the cobbles outside.

"For! For!" The joyous greeting rang out as eager young arms pulled the soldier into the cottage. "You are home again, For!"

But Ane Marie was upset at sight of her husband's drooping shoulders.

"Come now, a little hot soup will put new life into you," she cried.

As she fanned the fire to a blaze, bringing the pot to a boil, Hans leaned close to his father to catch his words.

"We got no further than Holstein when peace was declared. And I have not come home a lieutenant," he murmured sadly.

Hans looked up with a merry smile and his eager hands reached for the little theater.

"No matter, For. Look! I will show you my new puppets, and you will laugh when you see them dance and speak in such a funny way!"

How good it was to hear the hammer ring again in the little

cottage. And the evenings were a delight, with the cobbler taking a hand with the puppets, adding words in a foreign tongue.

"You shall gain by my travels, my son," said he. "And one day you, too, will journey far into the world, to see how other people live and speak. 'Tis a fine education for a man."

But now, after a few years had rolled by, a sad sickness stole into the little one-room cottage. Quietly the neighbors came to bring their herbs and say their prayers for the unhappy shoemaker. But nothing could be done to help him, and in the twilight of the third day, he slipped far away to another world.

Hans could not believe that his father had left him, never to return. Off to the beeches he wandered, where he could throw himself under the kindly trees, and weep his heart out for the dearest companion who would walk with him no more.

"For! For! For!" His cries cut deep into the shadowy silence of the little grove where he lay.

Only a sigh came back to answer him, as a breeze bent the strong arms of the watchful trees closer around him.

CHAPTER TWO

THREE giant mill wheels stopped their noisy churning with a loud whish — sh — sh — sh. There was water enough and to spare in the shadowy pond. Enough for all the washings in Odense, if the neighbor women had a mind to use the sunny morning hours.

Hans Christian's eyes lighted as he opened the door of his new home on Monk Mill's Gate, where Ane Marie had taken a second husband. With so much water, his voice should ring round the whole world!

"Whoo-ee! Whoo-ee!" His glad shout startled the birds as he raced down the narrow path to the mill. Into the pond he leaped with a splash and shivered as the icy water licked at his legs.

Out on Ane Marie's favorite washboard rock he dug his toes into the holes and began to sing. The flood of golden tone poured from his throat. On down the stream and over the waters of the mill pond it echoed, clear and sweet and strong.

Along the mossy banks, neighbor women straightened

their weary backs and sat on their heels to listen and applaud.

"It's that young Andersen boy. Thinks he'll be a great singer some day, I reckon."

"Singer! Big enough now for hard work, I'd say."

"Already tried it, Fru. Went with my boy to the factory and spent his time acting out plays. Men laughed and called him a girl. So he ran away home and hasn't been back since."

"Nay! Nay! Nay! Mother better find him harder work, I say."

But Hans was never so happy. A fine audience he had this bright morning. The moment his singing stopped, a cry rang up and down the river bank.

"More, boy! Give us another!"

Grinning with delight, the young singer bowed in all directions and again poured out his heart to the lovely fresh morning. A sudden splash at his feet stopped the warbling, and in an instant Hans's fingers closed swiftly around a fat wiggling fish.

"For your supper, Fru!" he chuckled. Wading ashore, he held out his slippery catch to a pale little neighbor woman.

"Bless me! Such luck, and so early in the morning!" Her thin voice cracked as she wiped her icy fingers on her apron. "Biggest meal for me and my old man in many a day."

Hans laughed happily and squatted down beside her.

"A secret, boy!" The little old woman leaned toward him, lowering her voice. "Did you know that beneath that very rock where you were standing, far down under the earth, lies the great land of China?"

Hans sat up quickly, his blue eyes wide.

"China!" he breathed. "Then perhaps a royal prince down there has been listening to my songs!" He edged closer to the snow-haired figure and eager words poured into her astonished ears. "Some night, when you are snug in your bed, he might dig his way up through the earth to find me. In a flash of green lightning he would carry me back with him, down, down through the earth to China!"

The little old woman listened with all her ears as Hans went on. "A fine and noble prince he would make me, Fru. Rich and powerful I would become. Then one clear day, with the wind blowing north, he would allow me to come back to Odense. In the center of town, a great castle I would build myself to live in. You would be the first to come to my door, and you would say, 'Bless my silver buttons, if it isn't the cobbler's son!' "

Hans rocked back and forth, his eyes half closed.

"You would make a deep curtsy, and I would say to you, 'Arise, my lady! I pronounce you Neighbor Queen. Behold your dress of satin and lace, with ruby crown on your proud white head!' "

That very evening, as soon as the moon rode high overhead, Hans crept down through the garden to the water's edge. The Prince of China might be waiting below for the sound of his voice!

Lifting his face to the star-filled heavens, he began to sing with all his might. The beautiful clear tones rang through the night in one haunting song after another.

As he stopped for a moment, voices from the house next door called out to him.

"Bravo, young singer! Come, let us have a look at you."

Picking his way through the shadows of the tall black hedge, Hans blinked in the bright lights of the great manor house. Like a fairy world it was, with fine ladies and gentlemen in rich costumes, smiling down at him.

"You like us, then?" the kind voice of a handsome man questioned him gently.

"Oh yes, sir. You may even be the prince from China!"

A burst of low laughter greeted his words.

"A song! A song!" the call went round the richly-furnished room.

Hans beamed on the gathering. These people were his friends. Raising his chest in the tight, patched gray jacket, he sang on and on for the fine company.

"Wonderful! The voice of a nightingale. The boy is sure to make his mark with such singing."

Coins were showered on him, and holding them tightly in his fists, Hans bounded home through the shadows, calling as he ran.

"Mor! Mor! We are rich. See—the people yonder gave them for my singing!"

Carefully Ane Marie counted the shining pile dumped into her lap.

"Child! It is too good to be true. Such fortune I never dreamed of!"

Hans spun in circles on his heels, and swooping suddenly, wound his arms around the bent shoulders.

"I will take care of you, Mor. You will never have to wash on the river stones again."

Ane Marie sighed and patted the scraggly locks near her own.

"You are a good son, my child; the best a mother ever had."

Early the next morning, Hans was wakened by the rain pounding fiercely above him. What a good day to read books at neighbor Bunkeflod's! Plays he must find, plenty of them, to recite for the grand folk at the manor house.

Off through the driving storm he fled like an arrow and stopped, panting, at the green door of a fine old home. The little minister's wife, her kind face peering out of her ruffled cap, quickly drew him inside.

"Soaked to the skin, boy! Off with the coat and socks this very minute!" she cried. "Now then, by the fire you shall bake until the chill is out of the bones."

Fru Bunkeflod and her sister hovered over him, wrapping him snugly in a great woolen shawl. From the kitchen they pattered with steaming rich soup, pieces of bread and meat floating on the top.

Hans beamed up at them, his face like a sunray.

"My fairy godmothers!" he declared happily. "And I will never forget you, not even when I am a great man some day."

His eyes swept hungrily over the rows of volumes lining the walls. "Do you think I will ever have coins enough for books like these?" he asked wistfully.

Fru Bunkeflod put a heavy volume into his lap and patted the bony shoulders.

"To be sure! A whole house full of books," she comforted. "Bless you, boy. Read as long as you like."

With a happy sigh, Hans settled himself with the plays, the name "Shakespeare" printed in large letters on the cover. There were ghosts and witches to his heart's content, and on and on he read, shivering with delight. At last a cheery voice at his elbow startled him.

"Come now, boy. A bit of stew before night shuts down."

As he ate hungrily from the brimming plate, Fru Bunkeflod read aloud verses that her good husband had written.

" 'Tis a great honor to be a poet, Hans," she declared. "And a good work to write plays and stories. But to do them well, one must learn many things. Try hard to go to school, boy."

Hans listened carefully, his tousled head on one side.

"Oh, I learn much at the charity school," he declared. "And so many Bible verses I can recite, that this very Sunday I will become a member of the church!"

He got to his feet quickly. "And just think, Fru – I will have a new pair of real leather shoes to walk down the aisle! Come to the church and see for yourself."

Early Saturday morning he was in the cobbler's shop, his face wreathed in smiles as he gazed down at his feet, bound tightly in shining black leather.

"They will have a good squeak, Herr?" he asked, listening anxiously as he trod up and down.

"A squeak!" The cobbler was never so puzzled. "Many things I can put into a pair of shoes, but a squeak, now—."

"Oh, but they must make a good noise, sir, so that everyone will know I have new shoes!"

Sunday morning slipped quietly into peaceful little Odense, and Hans was the first one stirring in the tiny cottage. With loving hands he took from the peg Big Hans's coat that had been cut down for the special occasion. How good it felt on his back, warming him through and through. With his new shoes dusted and dusted again, he was ready and quickly ate his breakfast of hard bread.

Over the cobbles he swung along in the pale sunlight, listening proudly to the squeaking boots as they kept time to the pealing bells.

Pushing open the heavy church door, he looked carefully around him. The seats were almost filled now, and far down in front, solemn boys and girls sat waiting for the service to begin.

How still it was in the dimly-lit church! Hans smiled. He had come just in time. Bending down, he carefully tucked his trouser legs into the tall, shining boots. Now everyone would be sure to see them.

Squaring his shoulders, he lifted his head high and began

the long walk down the aisle. Squeak – squeak. Squeak – squeak. Squeak–squeak. The new leather whined and wheezed as everyone craned his neck to look at the polished shoes.

"What a horrible din! Why, it's the Andersen boy. Did you ever hear such noisy boots!" whispered the church folk.

Slowly, slowly, down to the very front row went Hans, his heart thumping for joy. No need for worry, – everyone in Odense knew now that he had new shoes.

All through the service he admired his treasures. Even in the long prayer, he peeked through his fingers to see if they were still shining. But Henrietta Wolff, the pretty, hunchback girl beside him, scowled hard at him.

Hans hung his head in shame. "Excuse me, God," his lips moved quietly, "for thinking of anything but You. My shoes can wait until tomorrow. Amen."

During the long sermon, he looked quietly at his companion. Such a rich little girl she was, with thick, pale golden curls. No doubt Ane Marie had washed her beautiful white dress on the stones and ironed it with great care for the special service.

Hans's lips pressed together in a hard line as he said to himself, "But she couldn't have as much fun as I have. She can't make puppets and plays and songs."

Back to the cozy house of Fru Bunkeflod he went each day after the neighbors' errands had been run. Book after book he read without stopping. Then home he would take himself to his beloved theater, to make new characters and act out the plays and stories he had just finished.

Ane Marie, watching the neat little clothes come swiftly

from his hands one morning, exclaimed with great delight.

"Child! Child! With such snippeting and stitching, you could become the finest tailor on the whole island of Fyn!"

Hans's needle dropped and he pushed the long yellow hair from his eyes. "But Mor," he answered slowly. "didn't you know? I am going to be a great actor some day. See – I have already written a play!"

His long arm swept under the pile of puppets and brought out a thick roll of papers.

"Listen, Mor," he cried, leaping to his feet, his eyes bright. "I will read it to you."

Ane Marie got up quickly. "Tonight, Hans. Tonight I will listen. It's time for the washing now."

But someone must hear his new play. Putting the roll under his arm, he sauntered out into the winding cobbled lane, spattered with fresh sunlight. Halfway down the street he stopped, and tapping on a neighbor's door, entered.

"'Morning, Fru Orsted," he greeted her cheerily. "I have come to read you my new play."

Without waiting for a reply, he began his *Abor and Elvira.* Walking up and down the small room, his eyes flashed and his cheeks glowed. His voice rose in excitement and sank to a whisper when at last every character was dead.

"But it is so sad, Hans," sighed his neighbor, rocking anxiously in her stiff-backed chair.

The young actor stood over her, his face solemn.

"God put the words into my mind, Fru," he answered gently. "So I can do nothing about them, you see."

Up and down the street he rambled, reading his play to anyone who had time to hear it.

Fru Bunkeflod put down her ironing at once and listened closely, watching the thin, fourteen-year-old actor pour out his heart in the sad lines. When he had finished, she filled his hands with sweet cakes and patted his head kindly.

"Ah yes, Hans, the work is good," she decided, folding her hands across her snowy apron. "But how fine it would be to go to school and learn to write even better plays."

School–school–school. Everywhere he went, the cry was always the same. But there was no money, and Ane Marie had done what she could in keeping him neat and clean for the charity school in the church.

One evening, after he had finished reading his new play for the fine folk at the manor house, a stately gentleman near him began to speak, startling him almost out of his wits.

"Something must be done for this Andersen boy. I will arrange for Prince Christian to hear him next week."

Prince Christian! The news spread like fire through the village.

"Did you hear? The Andersen boy goes to the palace! The shoemaker's son will appear before the Prince!"

Up and down the river bank washerwomen talked of nothing else. The moment Hans stood on his mother's washboard rock to practice his songs, a crowd gathered around to listen and point to the boy who would soon go to the royal palace.

His good friend, Fru Bunkeflod, soon heard the news.

"It is well, Hans Christian," said she thoughtfully. "If His Royal Highness will send you to school for a fine education, you can be well content the rest of your days."

Such a time as there was in the simple cottage at Monk Mill's Gate in getting ready for the rare visit.

"If only your father could see you now!" Ane Marie looked with pride into the freshly-scrubbed, shining young face. "To think of our son in the royal household!"

Off to the palace went Hans, his heart pounding with joy. Through the great doors he followed the guard and was startled at hearing his name announced in loud tones.

"HANS CHRISTIAN ANDERSEN!"

Down a long hall he walked and there, before him sat the Prince.

Without waiting a moment, he began to recite. Not once did he stumble in his lines and his voice rose to the rafters in loveliest song. The long room echoed with the clear, haunting tones, telling of Denmark's glory in the folk melodies of her people.

When he had finished at last, the Prince motioned his visitor to him. Now would come his reward!

"You bring me pleasure this day, Hans Christian Andersen. Tell me, boy, what would you like more than anything in all the world?" The royal Prince asked his question slowly, tapping the arms of the chair as he spoke.

"Oh, sire, I would like to go to a fine school, where I could learn to make better plays!" Hans's words rushed out as he locked his bony fingers together tightly. "And I would learn to sing and dance well, so that some day I could be a great actor!"

A frown darkened the brow of the Prince and his fingers beat faster on the arms of his chair.

"An actor! Not a calling for a poor boy, surely." His voice was hard. "Besides, such a school would be very costly. No, no. You must forget the idea, boy. A sensible trade you must learn, to help you to earn a good living when you are a man."

A trade! A sensible trade! The words rang in his mind as poor Hans left the room and slowly made his way back to the little house on the river.

Ane Marie met him at the door, her eager words calling out to him.

"He will send you to a school, Hans? He will give you a fine education?"

"No, Mor. He says I must learn a trade."

Ane Marie put an arm around the drooping shoulders.

"Ah well, it is best, child. Now you shall become the finest tailor on the whole island of Fyn. We must see about it at once."

Hans sprang back, his face white.

"No, Mor, no! Not yet!" Striding to his low cot, he reached underneath for the yellow clay bank. With a blow it was broken and with trembling fingers Hans counted the coins.

"See—it is enough!" he cried. "Thirty whole shillings! Now I can go off to Copenhagen and see something of the world before I begin to learn a trade."

"Copenhagen!" His mother threw up her hands. "But it lies across the big water! And who knows what would happen to a boy, alone in a great city?"

Hans's laughter echoed in the darkening room as he threw his arms about Ane Marie.

"Look at me, Mor!" he cried. "I am big and strong and can look after myself now."

With a sad and fearful heart Ane Marie made ready the little bundle of clothing early the next morning. All that she held dear was leaving the cottage, and at the very thought, her eyes filled to overflowing.

Suddenly she paused as a shadow darkened the doorway.

"Bestimor!" Cheery little Grandmother, in her one good dress and bonnet, had come to say good-by.

It was time to leave, and the three walked quickly down the road and beyond the city gates. There sat the coach driver, ready to pick up his young passenger for half fare, thanks to Ane Marie's bargaining. Tears fell fast as the three stood together, their arms close about one another.

"God keep you safe, boy, and send you back to us soon — soon."

The horn blew a shrill blast, and leaving his dear ones, Hans climbed up with the driver. Waves of loneliness swept over him as he clattered away in a great cloud of dust. Wiping his eyes on his coatsleeve, he turned to watch the two figures.

"Copenhagen, eh?" The stout driver clucked the horses on to a trot. "Stayin' long?"

Hans sat up straight, his spirits rising a little.

"Oh, yes. Until I become famous," he answered. Lowering his voice he went on, touching a packet over his heart. "Only this morning the village printer gave me a letter to the great dancer, Madame Schall. I will take it to her in Copenhagen, and when she sees how well I can dance, she is sure to find a place for me in the theater."

The bearded driver smiled at the eager young voice.

"Just so. Just so," he agreed, looking straight ahead. Pulling a half loaf from his back pocket, he held it out to his companion. "Bite of bread does a heap for a man's stummick, eh traveler?"

"Oh, yes. Thank you, sir!"

As the miles rolled by, Hans listened happily to the old man's tales and was sad, indeed, to say good-by to the kind-hearted driver. Night had already closed down and going aboard the small steamer, he found his hard pallet.

Tossing and turning through the long dark hours, he tried to sleep as the vessel pitched and rolled and shuddered. Again and again Ane Marie's words echoed in his ears: "When you see the foaming waters at Nyborg, you will be glad enough to come home."

Darkness turned to dull gray at last, and the small boat landed at Zealand. White and spent, Hans hurried ashore and dropping to his knees behind a small shed, bowed his head.

"Thank you, God, for taking me safely over the Big Water. But please don't let me feel so alone. Help me, God. Help me. Amen."

Strangely comforted, he climbed into the waiting coach. Miles of bumpy roadway, villages, and farmlands rolled by, and at last he arrived at the end of his journey.

"The city of my dreams!" he called out to the passengers, his arm sweeping over Copenhagen. "There I will become a great man some day!"

Seizing his small bundle, he moved slowly over the cobbles as in a dream.

"Copenhagen! Copenhagen!" he breathed, his eyes on the great buildings and the crowds filling the streets.

Strolling into an open square, he stopped short. A man in tattered clothing was calling out his wares, offering bills to passersby. Then the big gray building behind him must be the theater!

Round and round it walked Hans, his breath coming short and fast. Inside these very walls he would one day become famous, and all the world would speak his name.

"Playbill! Playbill!" The peddler was at his elbow again.

"Oh, thank you, sir!" Hans took the paper with a smile and began eagerly to read, when the man pounced upon him with a loud cry.

"Robber! Beggar! Thief! You take my wares and offer no pay? Police! Police!"

Dropping the playbill, Hans ran for his life, not once stopping until he was far down the street.

Weariness and hunger swept over him, and making his way to a small inn along the canal, he found a room under the eaves. Crawling onto the hard bed, he counted his precious rix dollars in the sputtering candlelight. Ten, and not a single penny to spare for food.

Ah well, his good hard loaf would keep him until the next day. But no need was there, even for bread, with sleep stealing over him swiftly, taking him far away into another world.

The morning light crept through the narrow window over his head and stiff with the cold, Hans struggled to his feet. Peering through the dingy panes, he was surprised to find the sun so high. It was time to be on his way to the great dancer, Madame Schall!

His precious letter from the little Odense printer safely in his inside pocket, he started out, his brown coat brushed and shoes wiped until they shone. A large, tall black hat fell half way over his eyes as he sped along the canal and stopped at last before the home of the famous dancer.

Taking a deep breath, he climbed the stairs and fell to his knees. A little prayer was sure to bring him luck.

"Here, boy, buy yourself a bun!" A serving maid opened the door and flung a coin at his feet.

Hans's cheeks burned, and darting after her, he called, "Oh, no! No! I did not come to beg. Here–here is the coin." Taking the letter from his pocket he held it out to her proudly. "See–I come to speak with Madame Schall."

In a few moments he was standing in the fine quarters and there, before him was the most beautiful creature he had ever seen, lying on a couch in crimson velvet robe. The queen of the dance was reading his letter!

"So you want to enter the theater, Hans Andersen." A smile played around her lips as Madame Schall studied her strange visitor. "What character could you play for me now?"

Hans went to her swiftly, his long face alive with joy.

"Oh, madame, I would like to do Cinderella," he cried. "And if you will permit, I will first remove my shoes, to be light for the part."

In an instant he began to dance and sing. Leaping into the air, he whirled about the room in dizzy circles, his long arms and legs making sharp patterns as they kept time to his singing.

Madame Schall shrank back onto her couch, covering her eyes with her hands as the floor and furniture shook around her.

"Take him away!" she called, laughter pealing from her lips. "Take the monster away! I can bear no more!"

Hans stood in the center of the room, his hand over his heart.

"You–you do not like my dancing, madame?" His voice choked in his throat.

"Dancing? Surely you do not call this dancing!" she cried, her hands still covering her face. "You will never be a dancer, boy. Never!"

Hans found himself in the sunny doorway, the low voice of the serving maid drumming in his ears.

"Come to the back of the house when the dinner is over. There will be scraps from the table," she promised him.

But Hans scarcely heard as he clattered down the stairs and walked slowly back along the canal. "You will never be a dancer, boy. Never!" The words of Madame Schall rang over and over in his mind.

On he trudged, hardly knowing where his feet led him, when suddenly an idea made him stop in the middle of the street.

"Why have I not thought of it before?" he said to himself. "There is the director of the theater! Surely he will find something for me to do."

Back to the gray stone building he took himself, new hope stirring within him. Carefully wiping the dust from his shoes, he took his great hat from his head and rapped at the heavy door marked "MANAGER."

"Come in! Come in!" A harsh voice answered his knock. The dark-browed man behind the desk looked up in surprise at the visitor in ill-fitting, home-made coat.

"Your business, young man?" he demanded crisply.

Words tumbled from Hans's lips, one on another. "Oh sir, I have come all the way from Odense in a long and terrible journey. The wish of my life is to join the theater, and you may be sure that I can act very well. You have a place for me, sir?"

The big man pounded the desk with his right fist. "The theater!" he barked, his heavy eyebrows lowered in a scowl. "But you are far too thin, boy."

Hans sighed with relief. "Oh, sir—if you were to pay me a hundred rix dollars a week, I would soon be fat!"

The manager laughed heartily.

"As easily as that!" His voice filled the small room. "No, boy. In the theater we take only those who have had an education."

Hans's eyes searched the floor and color flew into his cheeks as he felt for the door.

Up and down the streets he wandered, hearing nothing, seeing nothing. Startled, he found himself back at the theater, where people were crowding through the doors. They were going to see a play!

Hurrying to the window he cried, "A ticket, please!"

The stairs were long to the top of the building, but the moment he found a place on the bench, his troubles were forgotten. With shining eyes he looked down on the red and gold fittings and the chandeliers with hundreds of glistening lights.

Up went the curtain and he caught his breath at the giant stage with its splendid scenery. Some day he would be a great actor, walking on those very boards!

Clasping his knees with joy, he leaned forward, not to miss a single word of the players. But sad, indeed, were the two young lovers, soon to part forever. Hans could not bear to see them so unhappy, and covering his face with his hands, sobbed aloud as the curtain fell.

Two old women on the bench turned to him in alarm.

"There now, do not take on so," they comforted. "'Tis only a play." Their lunch baskets were opened in a trice. "Here, boy—'twill put new life in you," they urged, pushing a fat sausage-roll into the grimy hands.

At their kind words, the tears only flowed the faster, and they listened in astonishment as Hans's troubles poured from his lips.

"This—this is my life!" he cried at the end, his arm sweeping over the theater. "Can you see that I could never go back to Odense to be a tailor, with stitching all day long?"

"Ah, yes. To be sure, lad." Strong hands patted his shoulders as the motherly women hung over him.

His pockets stuffed with good bread and butter and fruit and sweet cakes, Hans left the theater, promising soon to visit his kind new friends.

Lighter in heart than for many hours, Hans roamed down the street, enjoying such a meal as he had not tasted since arriving in the city. Nearing a little park, he sat on a bench to feast his eyes on the bright sunset. What did it matter if his money was all but spent? God would see to everything for him.

An old man in threadbare coat edged onto the rough boards beside him, eyeing the bulging pockets.

"Have a bite, sir?" Eager young hands held out the tempting array.

"Bless me! Bless me, now!" The little man chuckled as he crowded the good morsels into his beardy cheeks. "Haven't had such good fortune since my own children turned me out to beg."

His eyes were on Hans's shining face. "Heart as big as that sun goin' down yonder," he declared. "City's no place for a fine boy like you. What brings you here, lad?"

The tale burst forth again and when it was finished, Hans looked around carefully. The little park was quite deserted.

"Would you like to hear me sing?" he asked eagerly, moving away from the bench.

His hoary companion smiled good-naturedly. "Homesick many a month for an earful of good tunes. Pipe 'er up, boy!"

He nodded and chuckled and poked the earth with his stick cane as the songs rang out in the brisk evening air. Passersby stopped to listen, leaving coins which were hastily pocketed by the old man.

"Look here, young feller—" the stick whacked the bench suddenly—"Director of the Academy never had a better voice in the theater chorus. There's your chance, boy."

Hans spun round in a circle. "You think he would take me?"

"Yes, siree. Kinder-hearted man than Siboni never lived. Good luck, young 'un." The old man slipped away into the shadows, his pockets stuffed with what was left of the good snack.

The next morning it was still dark when Hans crept down the stairs of the inn, tall hat bobbing on his long yellow hair. He must practice his songs outside where no one would be disturbed, to be ready for the singing master, Siboni.

At the door, a curt command from the shabby woman at the desk, startled him.

"Rent due, young man. Six rix dollars."

Hans felt quickly for his precious coins. "Yes, madame. To be sure, madame."

She hung over him as slowly he counted out the money, her sharp eyes watching the last dollar go slowly back in an inside pocket.

"I—I will not be staying longer," murmured Hans. "I must go back for my bundle."

In a few moments he was at the door again, his small possessions under his arm.

"Breakfast, boy?" The voice at the desk was not so harsh this time.

"Breakfast?"

"Goes with the room."

If only he had known! Gulping down the hot coffee, he ground away on the chunk of hard bread, leaving not a crumb on the tin plate.

"One rix dollar. One, one, one!" beat in his mind as he trudged along the canal to seek the home of the famous music director.

But Herr Siboni would save him. His footsteps quickened at the happy thought. Yes, Siboni would surely save him from Odense, and tailoring.

CHAPTER THREE

FISHERMEN unloading their silvery catch, looked up startled as snatches of song floated down to them. Who would be singing along the canals at this hour of the day? Curiously they looked after the young stranger loping along with face turned to the rising sun, large stovepipe hat sliding around on his ears.

"Its 'im, the long young 'un," they agreed. "Fair tune, pardner! Rest awhile and give us another," they called. "Let's have ROARIN' GALE, LET 'ER GO, BOYS."

Hans smiled, and waving to the fishermen, went on with his practicing through the hours. By midday he was far across the city, standing at the beautiful doorway of the famous director. Doffing his hat, he bowed his head for a moment and pulled the knocker. His heart beat hard against his chest as a housekeeper in spotless apron, answered his call.

"Master Siboni?" she asked in surprise. "He is busy with friends. Come back next week, young man."

His last chance gone! Hans sprang at the closing door.

"Next week!" he cried. "But I shall be dead by then!"

The little woman turned sharply, a startled look on her round face. "Come now, boy. Nothing is as bad as that."

"Oh Madame, if only you knew! Herr Siboni, alone, can save my life!"

Kind ears listened as Hans poured out all of his troubles.

"There now, boy. Wait, and I will speak to the master."

Hans stood without moving where she left him, his eyes on the door. The minutes went slowly by, and still she did not return. Perhaps she would never come again, and all would be lost.

When he thought he could bear it no longer, he was startled by the sound of footsteps. There, looking down from the doorway was a group of men in fine clothing.

"I am Siboni." The handsome, tall master spoke gently. "Maria has told us about you. Perhaps you have come to sing for me?"

"Oh yes, sir—all the way from Odense!"

Clasping his hands together, Hans began the melodies so dear to his heart, melodies that Danish mothers had sung to their children for hundreds of long years. Haunting they were, tender and fierce and with a deep longing in them.

Carefully the master listened, and at last motioned for the singing to stop.

"Come in, boy," he invited, waving Hans into the sunny rooms. "The housekeeper tells me that you also write plays."

Hans smiled brightly. "I do, sir, and stories and poems, as well. I will recite them for you."

Siboni and his guests watched the young actor stalking about the room, his pale cheeks flushed and blue eyes bright as he lived the parts of his characters. So upset was he by their sorrows, that when their last words had been spoken, he fell into a fit of weeping.

"See here, Andersen," began the director quietly, his hand on the trembling shoulder. "There is some promise in the voice. How would you like to have some lessons with me?"

"Oh, Master Siboni, with all my heart!" Hans could scarcely speak the words. "And perhaps I could be in the chorus in the theater!"

"Not so fast, boy. We can tell nothing until we begin to work."

The director's friends gathered around with many kind offers of help.

"A little food would do the lad no harm," said the composer, Weyse, seeing the look of hunger in the troubled blue eyes.

Siboni turned to the housekeeper. "Maria, find a room in the neighborhood for the young man, and see that there is hot food at once."

Stumbling through the doorway, Hans found a place at the table in the kitchen, the good smell of hot bread filling the sunny room. Never did a meal taste so good. With a prayer of thanksgiving, he followed the cook to the tiniest room under the eaves not far away. Spent with excitement, he flung himself down on the clean little cot and was soon in the world of dreams.

Through the bright months, Hans was happier than he had

ever been. There was a singing lesson each afternoon, and in his small room at night he practiced the songs and exercises over and over again. And much he learned from the students who came to study with the famous teacher.

"Boy!" Master Siboni's voice rang through the house one morning. "A message to take to the composer, Weyse. I would like his answer within an hour."

A cold damp wind was blowing in from the sea, and Hans was glad to run most of the way. Knocking at the musician's door, a cheery "Come in! Come in!" took him inside the comfortable house.

"Hans Andersen!" exclaimed the composer, holding out his hand in welcome. "Oho — fingers like last year's icicles! Here—sit by the fire while I answer Siboni."

When the letter was finished, back to the chair he came smiling, his hands behind him.

"A secret I have been waiting to tell you, Hans. Some kind friends wanted to make you a little present. And so I have been keeping it here for you."

Onto the slender knees he laid a small leather sack, bulging with coins.

"You will find enough to buy warm clothing. And just in time, with winter around the corner, eh?"

Hans tried to speak, but the words would not come from his trembling lips.

"There now, boy—no need for thanks. Good luck to you!"

Flying over the cobbles, Hans climbed to his small room and poured the coins onto the bed. Seventy-six rix dollars!

Why, it was a small fortune. How pleased his mother would be! Seizing pen and paper, he could not get the words down fast enough.

> "Dear Mor,
>
> You cannot think what great luck has come to me! I am rich, with rix dollars to buy a great coat and trousers. When next you see me, I shall look like a King. Tell everyone in Odense that I am learning to Sing, and am Very Successful. I shall come home a Great Man.
>
> Your loving son
> Hans Christian.

"Fetch water, Hans. Meat from the butcher we must have at once. Woodpile getting low. Hurry, boy, lay the fires before the master comes down for his breakfast."

Poor Hans. No sooner was a task finished than another was begun. But happily he worked away, obeying orders through the long hours of the day. And well repaid he was, especially by the kind housekeeper, who rewarded him with fresh buns and cakes from the oven, and a taste of the special dishes for the guests.

"I need you, Hans!" A new voice was calling him one morning. In the beautiful salon he found the lovely young Marietta, paint brushes in hand. Before her was a long easel, and she motioned Hans to a chair nearby.

"You shall pose as my uncle, Siboni. See, I have already painted his head, but there is no time for him to sit for me while I do the body."

Quickly she draped a cloak over his shoulders and stood back to look at him.

"Oh, Hans!" she chuckled merrily. "My uncle so plump, and you like a beanpole. I shall have to stuff you!"

Pillows and more pillows were piled under the cloak, and the two laughed heartily as the stuffing went on. The master, hearing the gales, poked his head in the doorway and shouted with glee at his likeness seated in the chair.

"We must call the painting, 'Hans Christian Andersen Siboni'," he declared.

To while away the hours, Hans entertained pretty Marietta with stories, made up as he went along.

"In the far Northland, where the sun never shines all winter long, there lived a poor peasant and his beautiful little daughter," he would begin. "More than life itself the father loved the fairy creature, who was all that he had in the wide world. Like a sunbeam she flitted about the cottage, setting it in order with the help of her white kitten, Moppet, who was quite as tidy as she. One morning the good peasant awoke to find the wee maiden very ill, indeed. 'Take me to the Ice King, Father,' she sighed. 'Only he can make me well.' A great fear filled the heart of the poor peasant. The Ice King was miles and miles away in his palace of shining crystal, in the frozen white forest of the silent Northland."

Marietta would listen, her brush in air.

"Go on, Hans! Go on!" she would beg. And the tale would grow, the young artist forgetting all about her painting.

The months flew by, and when the March winds howled through the streets of Copenhagen, a hoarseness crept into Hans's voice that troubled him. Worst of all, the master would not let him sing, and Hans was sad, indeed.

"It will surely pass," he said to himself through the anxious days. But the rasping grew worse, instead, with a crack when he spoke that sounded very queer.

"The voice is changing," decided Siboni, listening closely for the last time. "It will mean no more singing for a few years, Hans, until the tones are settled." He sat at the piano, and as he pondered the matter, a sigh escaped his lips. "I can help you no longer, my boy. And so I must find someone else to take over your duties."

No longer was he needed in the master's house! The thought cut into his heart like a whip. Slowly Hans went off to his room to put his belongings together. With his precious puppet theatre under one arm, he made his way back to the kitchen.

"Never a better errand boy set foot in this house," declared the cook. "Right sad I am at losing you, my dear Hans. Now why not go to my friend?" she went on briskly. "Just a mile down the street you will find her. She may have a place for you to stay."

Bending his head to the cold, raw wind, Hans started out. The bulky box was hard to hold, and the little bundle of clothing kept slipping from under his arm as he struggled against the gale that almost swept him from his feet.

At last he came to a dingy grey house and an old woman wrapped in woolen shawl, opened the door a crack.

"You have money to pay?" she questioned sharply, her dark eyes looking over the young customer from head to foot.

"Oh yes, madame. Not much, but enough."

Suddenly Hans smiled and the door opened wider.

"Only a bit of a room, but 'twill do, I reckon. Come in, come in!"

Up the stairs to a low storeroom trudged Hans. As he felt in the darkness for a place to put his belongings, the old woman lighted a candle with trembling hands and set it on a bench.

"Ten rix dollars for rent," she grumbled.

Thrusting the coins in a worn sack dangling from her belt, she ambled down the stairs, muttering to herself.

Hans looked carefully around his new home. Old boxes and boards lay stacked in a corner and a lean mouse crept from under them to watch him with beady eyes.

Hans smiled. At least he was not alone. Half closing his

eyes, a little tale began to spin itself in his mind. "Once there was a mother mouse, a happy little creature, who lived with her babies on the edge of a grain field, far out in the country. One morning she called her black-nosed children around her, and tying on her bonnet, said to them: 'My dears, I am sad to think that you are growing up with nothing but a country education. And so I am on my way to town to see what can be done about it. Now listen well, my pretty mousekins five. Do not so much as wink an eyelash outside the house while I am gone!' Patting down the fur on her sleek sides, she gave a quick look around, and squeaked good-by. No sooner had she scurried around the corner than a loud THUMP! THUMP! THUMP! sounded along the dirt wall just outside the mouse's door."

The thrumming of the wind along the gables startled Hans from his story making. Bestirring himself, he undid his bundle and laid out his belongings on the pile of wood.

Wood! Lots of it, simply for the taking. What an idea! He would make real furniture for his puppet theatre. Humming a tune, he set to work and the hours sped swiftly by. Not until he felt a hollow ache inside him, did he put away his tool.

Down the stairs and along the cobbled streets he took himself, and his nose told him quickly enough when he had arrived at the baker's. In a trice he was in the clean little shop.

"Ah, my good friend, the poet Andersen!" greeted the short man with a smile. "New verses today?"

Hans shook his long hair slowly. "No, Herr Peter. But two plays you have not yet heard. The first begins this way——"

The baker looked at the clear, shining eyes in the delicate

face as the young boy's voice echoed through the room.

"Only beautiful thoughts in this boy's head," said he to himself. "But they'll never earn him much of a living."

As the lines came to an end, he quietly wrapped sweet buns in a paper and handed them to his visitor.

"A new kind of dough today," he declared, his eyes twinkling. "New tales from you and new dough from me!" he laughed gaily.

"Oh, thank you, Herr Peter." Out in the darkness, Hans tore off the paper and the buns disappeared like magic as he wandered along the quay.

Suddenly the lights of a large building glowed through the mist and he followed the people through the tall doors. In a long room, books lined the walls from floor to ceiling. Hans blinked his eyes. All the books in the world seemed to be gathered here.

On tiptoe he moved from row to row, his fingers touching them lightly as he eagerly looked at the printing on the back.

"Read as many as you like." A kind voice at his side made him look up quickly. The director, a gentle little man with white beard, smiled warmly. "And come as often as you like," he added. "All are welcome."

"Oh, sir, I would never be lonely here," answered Hans, his arm sweeping around the room. "And how much I could learn!"

Long winter hours Hans spent in pouring over the treasures in the library. He could not read fast enough as hungrily he turned the pages of one book after another. Verses of poetry made him sigh and laugh aloud for joy. Often leaving his place at the table, he would hurry to the old director.

"Only listen, Herr Nyrup!" he would exclaim, reading the lines in hushed tones. "Are they not the most beautiful you have ever heard?"

The old man nodded his white head, watching the eager face with delight.

"Ah yes, they are good. Take the book home with you, and these new picture books, as well."

With a cry of joy, back to his storeroom went Hans, the precious volumes under his arm. There were many ideas for his puppets and costumes and scenery, and gay folk songs poured from his lips as he set to work in the dim light of the flickering candle.

Springtime in Denmark! How good it was to leave his dark quarters and roam in the clear sunlight along the canals that he loved so well. He stood watching the gulls one morning, the clean, brisk wind sending his yellow locks flying, when a hand on his arm startled him.

"Herr Dahlen!" The master of dancing held out his hand in greeting.

"We have missed you at Siboni's, Hans. Tell me, do you still dance and sing, as you used to do?"

Hans was silent for a moment. "Why—you see, there is no audience now," he replied. Suddenly a light came into his eyes. "Perhaps you would let me dance in the theater some time," he cried. "Then what an audience I would have!"

Dahlen smiled. "And a good many lessons you would need before then, boy—months and months of hard work."

To Hans's great delight, dancing lessons with the great master, began. But often Dahlen looked at his young pupil in dismay.

"No, Hans! The feet do not jerk. Now we start again from the beginning. Toes pointed to the floor. Back straight, head up."

To the dancing school in the theater he took his charge, where for whole mornings poor Hans stood without moving, with nothing to do but hold a staff in his hand.

"If only I could dance in the ballet," he begged.

"Patience. The time will come," answered the master.

After months of waiting, his wish was to be fulfilled. Dahlen smiled brightly one morning as he put a playbill into the hands of his student.

"You see, your patience is rewarded," he declared. "I have just arranged a beautiful ballet, and you will have the part of a spirit."

The words swam in a mist before Hans's eyes.

"Mor will be so proud of me," he sighed. "At last I am beginning my life in the theater!"

That night the line on the playbill was read again and again in the candlelight: A SPIRIT — HANS CHRISTIAN ANDERSON.

Crawling onto his cot, he put the precious paper under his pillow and tried to sleep. But the line kept calling through his mind: A SPIRIT — HANS CHRISTIAN ANDERSEN. Hugging himself with delight, he lit the candle to see again how the words looked on the paper. Ah, there they were: A SPIRIT — HANS CHRISTIAN ANDERSEN.

The night of the performance arrived at last, and Hans put on his costume with the greatest care and took his place behind the wings with the band of spirits. The greatest wish of his life was coming true.

There was the call! With flying leaps he darted onto the stage before the bright lights. How good it was to feel the boards beneath his feet! And there were the crowds of people below, watching and smiling. They were looking right at him!

Hans sprang nearer the footlights, waving his arms in a

dance all his own. A burst of laughter greeted his solo and warmed with the applause, his feet twinkled faster than ever.

Suddenly Hans looked around as the music stopped. He was alone on the stage, his comrade spirits long since gone. In the merry laughter that swept in waves over the audience, he darted to the wings.

No one ever played a part with greater joy. But when the evening was over, the dancing lessons came to an end.

Two years in Copenhagen! Hans could not believe that so long a time had passed by in the great city. And how kind had been the friends of Master Siboni, seeing that there were just enough rix dollars to keep bread in his mouth and a roof over his head.

It was long, now, since he had paid a visit to Madame Rahbek. Much she had done since meeting him at the master's, allowing him a place at her dinner table once a week. He must go to call on her this very night. And no better time to wear the fine jacket just given him by the choir-school director.

Buttoning the blue coat swiftly, he looked down in dismay. The choir-director was a very plump man. Ah well, he must find something to fill out the chest.

Handbills were everywhere, and seizing a handful, he thrust them into the loose folds. Again and again the papers went in and Hans smiled happily as the wrinkles disappeared at last in the great lump on his chest.

The night was warm, indeed, and sauntering through the lamplit streets, he arrived at the spacious home and waited quietly on the doorstep.

"Hans Christian!" Beautiful Madame Rahbek shook his hand warmly and seated him in the fine salon with her guests. "This will be a rare evening," she explained gaily, "with our young Andersen to entertain us!"

At once Hans was on his feet, bowing to right and left. Crackle! Crackle! Crackle! The rustling of the handbills startled him and he straightened himself swiftly.

"Open your coat, young man," commanded the hostess, "so that you will be more comfortable when you recite."

Hans smiled feebly. "I—you see—there is no need, madame," he gasped. "I am quite comfortable."

What a terrible evening it was! As soon as he could leave, away from the beautiful home sped Hans, startling the strollers by plunging his hands into his breast and scattering clouds of papers into the swirling waters of the canal.

More than any other place in the great city, Hans loved to take himself to the peaceful, cozy home of the little old lady, Fru Bunken. There he could read by the hour rare old books, and talk of the works of the great writers.

"Come in, friend, come in!" The silvery voice welcomed him into the cheery rooms one evening, so far from the noise and bustle of the streets. "Some new poetry, or a play fresh from the writer's mind?" she cried, her hands reaching for the roll of papers.

Hans beamed with joy. "Oh, Fru Bunken, wait until you

hear my two plays! Only yesterday I sent copies to the director of the Royal Theater."

"To Herr Collin, the State Councillor of Denmark!" The old lady's cheeks were pink with excitement. "Come, share them with me at once!"

But when the plays were at an end, she sighed.

"Ah, my dear young Hans, one thing above all else is necessary: you must have an education if you are to become a great writer of plays."

There was silence in the beautiful room and a great sadness came over Hans.

"Then there is no hope for me, Fru?" The small voice came from the shadows.

"My dear boy, you must never give up hope—never!"

The days seemed endless now, and Hans walked along the canals through the hours. Must he, after years of waiting, go back to little Odense and become a tailor?

Wandering home through the half light one evening, he pushed open the door of his tiny room to find a letter awaiting him. Opening it quietly, he stared at the words that cried out to him from the paper.

His heart pounding in his ears, down the stairs he clattered, out into the night. Straight to the home of his good friend he went, the letter waving in air.

"It's come, Fru Bunken! It's come!" he cried, and read the words on the paper: " 'Herr Collin wishes to see Hans Christian Andersen at the office of the Royal Theater.' My plays will be given, after all!"

"Bless you, boy!" cried the little old lady, planting a kiss on the young flushed cheeks. "May you have the success you deserve so much."

The next morning Hans was standing before the tall, solemn director, his blue eyes fixed on the stern face.

"Your plays have been read, young man," began the State Councillor slowly.

"And you like them, sir?" Hans broke in eagerly, his face shining. "They will be performed in the theater, then, and I will have a part?"

"Slowly, Andersen, slowly," the quiet voice went on. "The plays are good, and show real promise. But more learning you need, and at once. I have asked King Frederic to send you away to school for three years. You will leave by the first coach for Slagelse. Good luck, young man. Write to me of any need you may have."

Hans found himself out in the sunlight, hardly believing the good fortune that had come to him so suddenly. His head felt light and his feet seemed hardly to touch the cobbles. In a few short hours he would be leaving Copenhagen to begin a new life.

CHAPTER FOUR

"ALL ABOARD!" The mail-coach driver blew a warning blast and Hans climbed up the creaky steps with the band of shoving, noisy students. Calling and shouting merrily, they waved farewell to everyone on the streets of Copenhagen.

"Where bound, Longlegs?" A freckle-faced boy scrambled to a place beside Hans, his blue eyes bright with mischief.

"To grammar school in Slagelse. This is the happiest day of my life!"

The grin faded suddenly from the round face as the boy sprang to his feet.

"Fellers! Longlegs is happy 'cause he's going to school!"

A shout of laughter greeted his words.

"Ho! Ho! Ho! A likely tale!"

Hans looked out over the glowing countryside and pretended not to hear. The sun swept the earth in a glory of light, and everywhere color danced in richest October hue. Who could be sad for long in such a feast?

Funny songs and stories abounded through the hours and at every wayside inn, Hans watched coat-tails flying from the coach. In a few minutes, well-dressed boys climbed in again, munching hot meat-rolls and juicy tarts.

"Not a single coin to be spared for pleasure." Herr Collin's stern words echoed through his mind.

"Have a bite, Longlegs?" Freckle-face held out a tasty jam tart.

Hans swallowed hard. "No—no, thank you. I—I am not hungry."

The hours rolled by, and how glad he was to arrive in the little village of Slagelse.

"Hans Andersen!" The cheery voice of the kind housekeeper welcomed him into his new home. "Follow me, sir. I hope you will find your new room comfortable."

With a joyous cry, Hans strode to the window framed in snowy curtains.

"Think of it—a room with a real window!" he exclaimed. "I am the luckiest boy in the world!"

Hungrily his eyes swept over the rolling meadows, dotted here and there with gnarled, wind-blown trees. Everywhere was peace and quiet. Surely he would be happy in this place.

The clanging of a bell roused him and down the stairs he clattered to hot potato pancakes and bread and milk and honey. Like a royal feast it was, especially after a long day without food.

"Thank you, God, for being so kind to me," he murmured as he climbed at last into the clean little bed and fell fast asleep.

The sunlight and singing of birds wakened him early the next morning. With a bound Hans was on his feet, filling his lungs with the sweet, pure air. His first day of school was at hand!

But his heart sank at sight of his classmates. Towering over the seven-year-old boys, he felt like a giant. At their giggles, Herr Meisling rapped sharply.

"This is no time for laughter. Lessons will begin at once. Arise, Hans Andersen, and give me the sum of these numbers."

Chalk scratched on the board and small hands waved around the new pupil.

"You do not know the answer?" The angry voice of the headmaster beat on his ears. "Then the little boys will tell you."

When the long hours were over, Hans stumbled to his room. He knew nothing, not even as much as the youngest boy in the group. What would Herr Collin and the King of Denmark think of him?

In a fever, he sat at his small table and bent over his books. Through the hours he poured over the pages in the candlelight, reading until his eyes smarted and he longed for sleep.

Weeks and months went by and many of the teachers were kind to him. All but the headmaster.

"Stupid! Stupid!" he would shout at Hans's wrong answers. "If you do not do better, what reports will the State receive of you?"

Still longer hours Hans spent on his work. At night, when he could think no longer and his eyes began to close, he crept down into the garden. Round the cottage he ran, swinging his

long arms, and deep into the icy water of the rainbarrel he thrust his head, chasing sleep far from him.

If only he could put down the stories and plays that turned over and over in his mind, how much it would help. But the warning of the schoolmaster, "Remember, boy, there is no time for foolish writing," made him bend swiftly over his lessons.

One night he could stand the longing no more. Out came a clean sheet of paper and words sprang from his pen. Faster!

Faster! He must get them down before they slipped away.

Red spots glowed on his cheeks and his heart was warm within him when the poem was finished at last. Across the top he wrote: "The Dying Child."

What did it matter if his lessons were unfinished? Happier than he had been in long months, he stuffed the paper under the mattress and crept into bed. Dreams of the bright days of his childhood filled his mind, and he was sad when the daylight brought them to an end.

The poem! Quickly he found the crumpled sheet and thrust it inside his shirt where no one would see. All through the long hours, when the angry voice of Herr Meisling shouted at him, his hand flew swiftly to the paper near his heart to bring him comfort.

He would feel even better if he could share his verses with someone. As soon as the evening meal was finished, off to his neighbor he sped, and a small group was soon gathered around him.

"A poem! The young student has written some verses!"

In clear tones Hans began to read the lines. How good it was to have an audience! The sad tale went on and when it was ended, there were tears in the eyes of the listeners.

It was good! The poem was good! His heart singing for joy, Hans crept home and to bed.

But the next morning, no sooner had he taken his place in the schoolroom than the master strode to the bench, his face dark with anger.

"So you disobeyed the rules!" he cried, bringing down his

long stick with a crash on the desk. "Now then, for seven whole days you shall see no one outside this room. Perhaps that will teach you to stop making silly poems, young man."

The long week was over at last, and he was free to spend Sunday as he chose. With spring in the air, Hans decided to tramp the ten long miles to Soro, where lived the well-known poet, Ingemann.

The fields were emerald green under the washed blue of the sky, and with the first tender leaves uncurling, the country was like a fairy world, clean and fresh and new.

Throwing back his long yellow hair over his shoulders, Hans laughed joyously as his legs ate up the ground. It was good to be alive on a morning so beautiful.

As he strode along to the singing of birds, poems filled his mind and he said them aloud. Then back over them he went, changing a word here and there, until they were just to his liking. When at last he arrived in little Soro, three were finished and he sighed with contentment. Now, if only the poet would like them, he would be happy, indeed.

Asking his way, he stood before the tiniest vine-covered cottage and knocked gently. A low voice answered from the shadows.

"Welcome, friend, and enter."

Just like a fairy tale, thought Hans, and laughing lightly, bent his head. There sat the poet and his wife at their midday meal of cheese and bread and honey and milk.

"Come, share our simple fare," they invited him, pulling up a chair to the snowy cloth.

"Oh, thank you, sir! I am Hans Andersen, and I have walked all the way from Slagelse, and—bread would be good." The words rushed out as he sat down. "On the way I made some poems. Would you like to hear them, Herr Ingemann?"

"Always a glad ear for poetry, Andersen. Begin, boy."

Hans never took his eyes from the kind face. Surely here was a friend, someone who would understand. One word from such a master would mean much to him.

Ingemann listened carefully as the lines went on to the end.

"Ah yes, Hans, you have the true heart of a poet. Keep on, boy, and find time to write a little each day."

Out on the lake they rode in a small boat and Hans listened in purest joy as the older poet, in deep rich voice, recited his own well-loved verses.

Back to the cottage trouped the three at sunset for sausage-cakes and wine.

"You have found another home, Andersen. Come as often as you like."

Hans's eyes shone as he shook hands with the master poet.

"In two weeks I go to Odense for Easter. There will be much to say when I return!"

Back over the fields he went, his heart warm at the thought of the kind new friends in the tiny cottage. There would be news indeed, to tell them on his return from Odense.

Odense! Hans whistled a gay tune at the thought of going home. Mor would be there to greet him! But there was no room in the cottage, so he would stay with the old printer, Iversen. And he would spend rare hours with Colonel Guldberg, one of the leading citizens of the town.

Every moment from then on, Hans could think of nothing but going home to Odense. Again and again the rule was banged down on the desk before him.

"Andersen! Always dreaming!" shouted the director. "What has come over you, boy?"

But at last the day came when he was free of the schoolroom and Herr Meisling. It was too good to be true. On winged feet Hans took his small bundle and was on his way. The sea was never so blue nor the sky so clear as the morning the little boat landed on the tiny island of Fyn. Soon, now, he would be in Odense! With clattering boots he climbed up beside the old driver.

"Bless my soul, you be the same boy I carried a few years

back!" The coachman slapped his knees with the reins. "Sure thing! Same long nose, big ears, and yellow hair. Only more drawn out, like. Would'a knowed ye anywheres!"

Hans grinned happily. Then everyone in Odense was sure to know him.

When they rounded the last bend in the road, he sprang to the ground and began to run toward a little figure coming slowly to meet him. But as he ran, Hans looked more closely at her. How bent she was in her flowered calico dress, walking along so painfully with her stick.

"Mor! Mor! Mor!" Sweeping her into his long arms, he held his mother close.

At last Ane Marie brushed away her tears and looked long at her son.

"Hans, my own Hans!" she sighed proudly. "Why, you are a gentleman now, with boots on, and real learning in your head!"

Into the road the neighbors flocked, calling out their greetings. "The Andersen boy has come home! Look you now—the shoemaker's son is like a count!"

Hans was never so happy, talking to everyone of the time when he was a boy, and visiting all the old places that he knew and loved so well.

Old Iverson, the printer, smiled at his guest for the night.

"Oh sir," Hans was on his knees, eager hands untying his small bundle, "some verses here I would like to read to you."

Low laughter rumbled through the comfortable cottage.

"Still needing an audience, boy? But come now, the good wife and I are ready to listen."

Hans towered over his kindly hosts, a pile of papers in his hands.

"You see, it is forbidden at the school to write my poems. But at night, when I am too lonely, I make verses about Odense, and am happy again."

The printer nodded his white head. "Always thought the yellow-haired Andersen boy would make the world listen to him some day," he declared, puffing away on his long pipe.

Ane Marie did no washing these days, and the brown calico dress was never worn so much. To the neighbors she went visiting, talking of nothing but her son.

"My Hans is off with the gentry. Oh, he is a fine gentleman, now," she would say, smoothing her flowered calico over her tired knees.

But what a day it was when Hans rode along the river in a boat with the leaders of the town. Ane Marie's stick tapped on the stones as she hobbled up and down the street.

"Quickly—to the river!" she called. "A sight you may never see again."

On the bank, she pointed to the boat with trembling, gnarled fingers.

"There!" she cried. "There is my son, Hans Christian Andersen, spending the day with the fine Colonel Guldberg and the mayor, himself!"

The holiday was over all too soon and sadly Hans visited everyone for the last time and began the journey back to Slagelse. In his little room he worked harder than ever at his studies, with difficult Latin and Greek to be mastered, as well.

The long months wore on and Hans was proud, indeed, when he was at last at the head of his class. How pleased Herr Collin would be! Out came the letter that had just come from the Councillor, telling his charge that he would spend the Christmas vacation with the Wolff family in their beautiful home in Copenhagen, just across from the king's palace.

Several times Hans had gone for an evening's visit. And who could ever forget Colonel Wolff? But Henrietta would be there to greet him. The same rich, golden-haired girl who had sat beside him in the Odense church and scowled at him when he had admired his new shoes during the long prayer.

Hans looked down at his shabby boots and worn coat. Surely he must have new ones before he could spend the holidays in such a splendid home. Taking his pen, he put down the words slowly.

"Dear Herr Collin, This is a very hard letter for me to write. But first of all, you will be glad to know that I have passed the examinations very well, indeed. Herr Meisling seems a little pleased with my work. Now for the bad part of this letter. I am sorry to tell you that my boots are in holes and let in water daily, so that my feet are hardly ever dry. May I beg for a new pair? Also my old coat does not hang together now and you would not care to see it on my back. It is harder for me to ask than you could ever know. But I would thank you over and over for your kindness my whole life long, if only you could send me funds for the shoes and coat. Your grateful

Hans"

He had not long to wait for an answer, and his heart sang for joy as he made himself ready for the journey. With a little shiver of delight, he slipped into the new, bright blue coat and shining boots and was on his way.

Christmas was in the air when he arrived in the big city, and a light snow was falling as he crossed the open square and stood at the doorway of the gray stone palace. How proud Mor would be if she could see him now. "Just like the son of a count," she would say.

A footman in red and gold livery opened the door and a cheery voice called down the stairs.

"Hans Christian! Welcome! I am here, in the library."

There sat Henrietta, the little hunchback, before the bright fire.

"It is so good to see you again, my friend," she cried, hands outstretched. "Quite a man of the world you have become since last you were here. Still writing verses?"

Hans's cheeks glowed, and searching hastily in his pockets, he handed her some scraps of paper.

Henrietta began to read, when suddenly she put a finger to her lips. "We must not let Father know. Remember the last time you were here?"

Hans smiled. "How angry he was after I had read my play for his guests. 'Rubbish, young man,' said he. 'You had better set your hand to a good trade, instead of trying to be a writer!'"

The two laughed together and Henrietta went on with her reading.

"But Hans, these are good poems, the best that you have written! Why not send them to the morning paper?"

Hans could only stare at her with round eyes. "You think they are good enough for all the people of Copenhagen to read?"

"Why not, my friend? At least we can find out."

At once the verses were sent on their way. But with the exciting days, they were quickly forgotten as people crowded into the beautiful home, bringing their Christmas greetings.

A giant tree was set up in the hallway below, and much

Henry C Pitz

laughter and joking there was as the family filled its branches with sweetmeats and rich trimmings.

"Like fairyland!" exclaimed Hans, looking in awe at the great spectacle.

Throughout the days, young folk of the neighborhood came to sing and dance around the proud tree. Hans laughed and shouted and sang with them, happier than a king.

Christmas Eve came all too soon, and he sat with Henrietta in the dimly-lit library beside a lovely tiny tree, all gaily bedecked in lacy white snowflakes. From under its branches she took a heavy package and handed it to her guest.

"The merriest Christmas in all the world," she cried.

Slowly taking off the paper, Hans exclaimed with joy at the handsome book, bound in richest leather. "The writings of the great Shakespeare!" he gasped. "Oh, Henrietta, how could you know that all my life I have longed to own even one of his works?"

A cheery laugh answered him. "But this may please you even more," said his little companion, putting into his hands a square, flat package.

A puzzled look came over his face. "The morning paper!" Hans was on the floor, turning the pages thoughtfully, when suddenly his eye lighted on two poems.

"My verses! See, Henrietta—they have printed them for all the world to read! Now I can die happily."

Her ringing laughter filled the little room. "Die, when your fame has just begun, Herr Author?" she cried, her brown eyes twinkling. "But quickly, Hans. Put the paper away where no one will see. In the morning we will play a little joke, you and I."

Christmas day dawned sharp and clear, with a clean blanket of snow carpeting the open square around the fine old house. Colonel Wolff had already taken his place at the head of the table in the spacious dining room, when Henrietta and Hans came in quietly.

"Ah, two Christmas angels to keep me company." His hearty, gruff voice greeted them as he glanced over his spectacles. "I trust you are enjoying the holidays here with us, Hans."

"Oh sir, I have never been so happy before. Everyone is so kind to me."

But the Colonel had already gone back to his paper. Turning the page, he looked up suddenly.

"Hm. Now this is good verse," he declared. Aloud he read the two poems, and taking off his glasses, looked hard at Hans. "There you are, young man. If you could write like that, it would be worth something."

When he had finished, Henrietta answered quietly.

"My dear father," said she with a mischievous smile, "the poems that you have just read, are the works of Hans Christian Andersen."

"Hm! Hm! Well, well, well! Hm!" grunted the Colonel. Flinging down the paper, he stalked from the room.

Henrietta quickly laid her hand on Hans's arm.

"Do not mind him, my friend. It is only his way. All that matters is that he liked your poems."

Each year in the beautiful home a grand ball was given. Even now the preparations had already begun and went on throughout the days until New Year's Eve, when the last gold chair was placed in the great ballroom.

Hans was in a flurry of excitement and hung over the banister to watch jeweled ladies in sweeping gowns of satin and lace, and men in solemn black, filling the rooms below. And there was the giant tree, glowing from tip to toe with hundreds of gleaming lights.

"Henrietta! Henrietta!" Suddenly he found her in her favorite little library. "Never have I dreamed that anything could be so beautiful!" he cried. "But you—you are not dressed for the ball?"

A bright smile lighted her delicate face. "I do not dance. My back, you see."

How brave she was, thought Hans.

"I will come often and give you news of the ball," he promised, starting to the door.

Quickly he went below, his bright blue coat brushed carefully. But everywhere, people looked at him from head to foot, a half smile on their faces.

What could be wrong? Suddenly Hans felt his cheeks burn and he crept off into a little side room to hide behind the long red curtains.

"It is my clothes!" he said to himself bitterly, "My country clothes. And heavy boots, instead of fine leather shoes."

With fists clenched, he paced up and down the room, muttering to himself. "Mind you, Hans Christian—one day you, too, will have fine black clothes. And people will smile and say, 'There goes the gentleman, Hans Andersen. What a coat he wears! No better to be found in the whole of Denmark.' "

"Andersen!" A voice broke in on his misery. "Colonel Wolff said I should find you somewhere about. I am Oehlenschlager. I wanted to tell you how much I liked your poems in the morning paper."

Oehlenschlager! One of the greatest poets in all Denmark! The two clasped hands and were friends at once. Long they talked together into the hours, forgetting all about the grand ball outside.

Hans sped on winged feet up to his room, his cares left behind him in the company below. He had made another friend, one who would bring him courage and comfort through the long years ahead.

Early the next morning a messenger arrived from Herr Collin, asking him to come at once to his home. Off through the deep snow Hans took himself, wondering why the State Councillor had sent for him before he had had time to pay him a call. Had Herr Meisling sent bad reports of him, after all? This might mean that no longer would funds be given to finish his education.

Arriving at the big, rambling house, he pulled the knocker and the door was opened swiftly. There stood Edward Collin, a boy his own age, looking out at him solemnly.

"Father is expecting you. He is there, in the library."

Hans found himself seated at a large table, waiting for the tall, silent man to speak.

The State Councillor looked at his young charge, tapping his long fingers on a pile of papers.

"Word has come to me from Slagelse, Andersen," said he. "The headmaster writes that you have done very well. I am proud and happy, indeed."

Hans sprang to his feet, the color rushing back into his face.

"Oh, I am glad, sir. And I thank you with all my heart for what you have done for me," he cried earnestly.

Herr Collin answered him quietly. "You have only yourself, and the State of Denmark to thank, boy. But there is another matter I wish to speak about. How would you like to finish your studies here, in Copenhagen?"

Hans stared down at the Councillor. "To—to leave Herr Meisling and the school, sir? Oh, that would be too good to be true!" The sound of his words stirred the tall man.

"My boy," he answered slowly, "I have only just heard from a young teacher at Slagelse how difficult your life there has been. But that is all ended, now. We will find a master for you here."

At the tears of joy in the bright blue eyes, Herr Collin rose, putting his hand on the young shoulder.

"You will stay with us for lunch, Hans. The children will be so happy."

Around the large table they sat, Edward, Ingeborg, and young Louise, who shyly pulled on his coatsleeve.

"You will play games with me afterward?" she begged, her brown eyes watching his face closely.

"Oh yes, if you like. But you will win. I can see that, even before we start."

Such laughter and romping as there was that afternoon in the back part of the house! Soon the neighbor children came in, begging to be a part of the fun.

"So, my chickadees, then come with me," commanded their leader.

A quieter game must be found, and motherly Fru Collin smiled as she looked into the nursery. There sat Hans, his long arms and hands making shadow pictures on the wall.

"It was a quiet night, with the moon well hidden in the tail of a dark cloud," his story began. "And old Brother Fox had a long, long way to go home. But so hungry was he that his poor stomach turned and whined inside him. 'Lack-a-day! Not a morsel of sweet young pullet have I tasted since sunrise,' he growled. 'But in the low henhouse of Mr. Farmer, yonder, I shall soon have my fill.' Slowly, quietly, he squeezed through the back fence. Not a feathered creature was stirring. Not a sound came from the blackness of the henhouse."

Nearer and nearer to Hans crept the children as the story went on. Edward and Ingeborg, with Herr and Fru Collin, stood in the doorway, watching with delight. When at last the shadow pictures were at an end, a great clamor arose.

"More! More! No—hide and seek!" The children were calling and scrambling over poor Hans, fighting for a place in his lap.

"Come, come now!" Ingeborg and Edward rescued the storyteller. "Poor Hans is tired. He will come again, but only if you let him go quietly."

Out into the sunset went Hans, his heart glowing with happiness. What a wonderful place the world was! He found himself dancing in the snow, whirling and kicking his feet high in air.

And to think that he would leave Herr Meisling and the noisy children forever! He stopped suddenly, and kneeling in the snow, raised his face to the setting sun.

"Dear God, you have been so kind to me. Some day I will repay all that I owe You. Thank you, God. Amen."

ORN
Henry C Pitz

How good it was to be back in the old city of Copenhagen again. Hungrily he sniffed the stale dampness of the canals, and the tar and the fish smells that were always there. And every cobblestone under his feet was more dear to him as the days went by.

In his tiny attic room, high up among the red-tiled roofs, Hans was happier than any king in his palace. Here he could be alone to work hard, and to dream when the stars came out at night.

His dreams went down on slips of paper, to be carried each morning to his new teacher, Müller.

"Verses, verses, and more verses!" said the kind tutor, smiling. "But let us see if you can work out the Latin and Greek as easily and as well."

To the Collins' his long legs took him often, where Edward helped him with his lessons. And whenever he forgot his lines, a sharp voice brought him back swiftly enough, with "Lazybones! Lazybones! To work!"

The year passed by on wings, and it was time to take the long examinations at the University. Hans was upset at the very thought, and studied for hours into the night. Morning found him tired and worn.

"Oh, Herr Müller, do you think I will be ready?" he asked anxiously each day.

"That is hard to say, my friend. But you must get more sleep, or you will never be ready."

At last the morning arrived, and his hands clenched in his pockets, he went off to the University. The door closed behind him and Hans faced the line of stern-faced men. How could he answer the difficult questions that they would ask him through the long, weary hours?

Edward and Ingeborg and Louise waited patiently for the sound of the footsteps they knew so well. At last, just at sunset, there was a shuffle and the door flew open. Laughing happily, Louise threw herself into the long, bony arms.

"You won the battle! I can tell by the way you feel!" she cried.

With a shout they danced in a circle around him, and soon Fru and Herr Collin joined the merry group. Hans went to Father Collin at once.

"I have passed the examinations, sir."

The State Councillor smiled his pleasure. "It is good, Hans. Now you will want to go on studying, no doubt, and learn to be something useful. A doctor, or a lawyer, perhaps?"

Hans stood rooted to the ground, his cheeks paling. "Why, sir," he faltered. "It has been settled in my mind for so long. I hope you will not be angry, sir, but I would like to spend the rest of my life in writing poems and stories and plays."

Herr Collin went to him quickly, hand outstretched.

"You shall have your wish, boy. Good luck to a new author!"

"Good luck! Good luck to my Hans, and all the tales he will write, just for me!"

Louise's voice rang through the rooms as she danced with him to the bright fire and the good hot supper waiting.

CHAPTER FIVE

HANS STOOD in his tiny attic room and stretched his aching back. It must be very early in the morning, with such a misty chill in the air. Shivering, he pulled on his homespun coat and a broad smile spread over his face.

At last he could tell his secret. Rolling together the scattered papers on his small table, he blew out the candle and opened the door quietly. Everyone in the house must still be asleep. Down the long stairs he carried his boots, not to disturb his neighbors.

How happy Henrietta would be! At the thought, a merry hunting tune piped from his lips as he strode along the canal. Long months he had been working quietly, shutting himself away from everyone for days at a time.

The square at last. In the gray light, the sentry looked at him sleepily as he guarded the King's palace. Klop-klop-klop. His heavy footfalls echoed hollowly in the damp morning as he crossed quickly to the princely home of the Wolff's.

"Hans Christian! What brings you out at daybreak? Lucky

you find me out of my bed!" Henrietta's cheery voice welcomed him from the dining room. "Quickly—another plate," she ordered the servant.

Anxiously she looked at her early visitor.

"Not a word until you have had food," she commanded. "Up all night, and not a bite to eat for days, I'll wager."

Speedily the heaping plate was emptied, and up to their hideaway sped the two. In the small library, Hans could keep his secret no longer.

"It is finished, Henrietta! I lay my offering at your feet, my princess."

Unrolling the papers, Hans read the parts of his new play, walking up and down and acting out the lines. Her eyes on his face, Henrietta sat listening, hands clasped tightly together. How could she wait until the end?

"Hans! Hans! Take the work to Herr Collin at once!" she exclaimed. "He will see that it is produced in the theater!"

Hans grinned at her happily, and rolling the papers together, was speedily on his way. But Herr Collin studied the matter more carefully, turning it over and over in his mind. Poor Hans sat on the edge of his chair, waiting with bated breath for the Councillor to speak.

His words came at last. "Great writers have hoped all their lives to have their plays given in the Royal Theater. And so you must not be too sad if the committee does not accept your work. Patience, boy. We will see what can be done."

Hans spent the anxious days in wandering along the canals. And each time that he sat at the Collins' table for food, he knew just by looking at the State Councillor, that no news had come.

Ah well, perhaps it was too much to hope for. With a sigh, he settled himself in his small room and again took up his pen.

He had not gone far one morning, when running footsteps sounded on the stairs outside.

"Hans! Hans! Open, man!"

There stood Edward, his handsome face wreathed in smiles. "Father sent me to tell you the good news!" he cried.

Hans caught his friend's arm, holding it fast.

"They—they will act my play on the stage?"

"Yes, Hans. The rehearsals will begin within a week."

Hans could scarcely contain himself with joy. To all of his friends he sped on winged feet, crying, "Have you heard? They give my play in the Royal Theater! You will be sure to come?"

At night, when he could not sleep, he found himself wandering through the streets to the theater square. Round and round it he walked, gazing with rapt eyes at the old grey building in the center. Was it possible that the dreams of the Odense boy were coming true at last?

The evening of the play arrived and in a flurry of excitement, Hans dressed carefully in his old brown coat and sped into the street.

A light April shower had just freshened the air, and as his long legs took him around the corner, he caught his breath. There, lying like a fairy jewel in the quiet waters of the canal, was the end of a rainbow.

A sign of good luck! Faster his boots flew along, skimming lightly over the worn cobbles as he neared the theater. Crowds were already pouring through the doors, and with fast-beating heart, he took his place backstage. Here he would be closer to the actors and watch his own play from the wings!

A round of applause greeted the first act and Hans listened as one in a dream. The people of Copenhagen liked his play!

Slowly the curtain came down at the end of the long evening, calls coming again and again from the audience.

"Author! Author!" Their cries reached him clearly above the clapping and ringing "Bravos!"

But now a sudden terror seized Hans and he seemed frozen to the spot.

"Andersen! Andersen!" The calling was louder. He must get away quickly. Blindly he rushed from the stage and ran into the street. On through the night he fled, straight to the home of the Collins'.

Stumbling through the darkness to the living room, he fell to his knees by an old armchair. Choking sobs shook him and he could not stop the tears that streamed down his cheeks.

"There, there, Hans!" A gentle, soothing voice came from a far corner of the room. "Do not mind too much if the audience did not like your play. You will write many others."

Mother Collin! Somehow he must answer her.

"Oh, no—no!" he gasped. "They cried 'Bravo!' I think I ran away because I was so happy."

And now, faster and faster his pen skipped over the paper. The people must like his new book, too. At last it was finished, A JOURNEY ON FOOT FROM HOLM CANAL TO THE EAST POINT OF AMACK, parts of it printed in THE FLYING POST for everyone to read.

Long months rolled by and one morning, finding Herr Collin alone, Hans shook hands warmly and seated himself behind the old desk.

"Good news for you, boy. Your book and play have brought you excellent returns, with funds to last a whole year."

With a startled cry, Hans was on his feet, new life surging through him.

"My first earnings!" he exclaimed. "Now I can have new clothes!" With a cheery good-by, he was off down the street and straight to the workshop of the tailor.

"A black suit, and of your finest material," he ordered the startled little man. "It must last until I am old and gray."

Across the city, the busy bootmaker put down his tools with a smiling, "Good-morning."

"New soles today, I suppose?" The kind old man shook his head at the tired boots. "Just in time, young feller."

"Oh no, sir. Whole new ones, and of your very best leather. This is a happy day for me, sir!"

No need to stay longer in the attic room that had served him so well. A man of the world must have fitting living quarters. With so little to move, it did not take long, and before nightfall he was happily settled in simple, airy quarters.

And now a whole new life began. Invitations came pouring into the sunny home, and in his fine clothes he spent happy evenings at the manor houses of writers and musicians and statesmen.

"A poem, Andersen! Let us have some shadow pictures! Tell us a good story!" the calls went round.

One morning, with the light creeping into his rooms, came the longing to see more of his native land. Besides, a new story forming in his mind, would take place in Jutland. Then why not go there for a little visit?

He was out of his narrow bed with a bound, and packing a little bundle, started on his way that very morning. As the miles dropped behind him, no happier person could have been found in the whole of Denmark.

Jutland! How beautiful it was in the July sunshine, its emerald shores washed with bright blue waters. Over the purple-heathered hills he roamed, stopping to peer down into the sparkling green fjords. His heart leaped at the glories around him, and down into his notebook went his PICTURES OF THE WEST COAST OF JUTLAND.

Back to dear little Odense he took himself joyously, straight to the home of printer Iverson to be greeted by his gentle, white-haired wife.

"You shall have your same bedroom with the flowers on the wall that you liked so much." Her voice was like a delicate silver bell. "If only the printer were alive to see you now, looking so well and happy. 'That yellow-haired Andersen boy will make a name for himself in the world,' he would say."

No sooner was he snugly settled in the cheery little room than a chorus of bright voices clamored in the hallway outside.

"Uncle Hans! Uncle Hans!" The tones grew louder as small hands beat on his door.

"Sh! Come away, you noisy children!" Fru Iversen was scolding gently. "You must not disturb him now."

Henry C Pitz

No more rest was there for the visitor that day, with little ones swarming over him, begging for more and more stories.

"Forgive me, Hans," laughed Fru Iversen, as she brought out jugs of ice-cold milk and mounds of spicy ginger cookies. "I should never have told them that Uncle Hans would be here with his bagful of tales!"

Wide-eyed children watched him closely now as his sharp scissors snipped into squares of folded paper. Lovely lacy patterns and designs fell in a white rain to eager outstretched hands.

"See the funny dancing men, bowing to each other! And the princess in her lovely tower is looking right at me. Here comes a mouse with her carriage and six. It's mine, mine, no—mine!" Shouts and delighted cries echoed round the cottage until Fru Iversen shooed away the noisy brood and locked her door for the night.

Long hours there were with Ane Marie, who sat in her calico dress, smiling happily as her son brought her news of his life in the great city of Copenhagen.

"You shall come for a visit some time, Mor, and a good guide you will find me," promised Hans.

Ane Marie shook her head and sighed. "Too far a journey for an old woman like me," she answered. "Odense is best."

Not far away across the sand dunes lived Hans's university friend, Christian. What fun it would be to pay him a little visit! Off he started the next morning, long before the sun was out of bed. Tramping the miles over the sandy hills, he arrived at the spacious home and walked through the open doorway.

With a startled gasp, a beautiful girl in snowy cap looked up from her breakfast.

"Your pardon, I beg you," said Hans gently. "I seek my good friend, Christian Voigt. He lives here?"

"Yes, he is my brother. And a lazy one at that, still in the land of dreams," laughed Viborg. "But come in, sir. You shall share my breakfast."

Never did coffee and bread and honey taste so good. In the peaceful, sunny room, Hans could not take his eyes from the delicate face near him.

The happy days flew by all too quickly, filled with picnics and boating and long walks in the moonlight. Ever at the side of the fair Viborg was Hans, listening to the music of her voice and watching the light playing in her deep violet eyes.

The joyous times came to an end and sadly he turned in the path to wave a last farewell to his good friends.

"We will meet again in Copenhagen!" Christian's sturdy voice rang over the dunes.

"Soon, soon. And you, Viborg, you will come to the city with your brother?" Hans called eagerly to the maiden.

"Perhaps!" Viborg's gentle laughter followed him as Hans strode back to little Odense.

The days and the nights were long for him now, filled with thoughts of the fair princess he had left behind him. And glad he was when autumn came and the mists settled low over the red housetops. Now he could go back to Copenhagen and wait for the lady of his dreams.

Quietly he slipped away to the city and was soon at work

at his desk, his pen sounding through the room as his Pictures of Jutland covered the pages before him.

At last one morning his heart leaped for joy at the glad news that his two good friends had arrived in the old Danish capital. Now he could ask the princess to be his forever, and live with him the rest of her days.

But the beautiful Viborg had other thoughts, and quietly sent back her reply. Poor Hans! Sadder than he had ever been before, and lonely, he looked around his little room that seemed cold and empty to him now.

His pen was silent and no laughter came from his lips. His feet dragged over the cobbles as slowly he wandered through the streets to the home of the Collins'.

"A story, Hans—a shiny new one before the call to dinner," begged Louise, pulling him to an easy chair and settling herself comfortably on his knees.

"Another time," he promised her, a far-away look in his eyes. "The tales have all flown to the moon."

Something was wrong, indeed. Herr Collin watched carefully as Hans, his face white and tired, scarcely touched the hot food on his plate. When the dinner was over, he spoke to him quietly.

"My boy, how would it be if you were to go off on a little journey? Six weeks in Germany, perhaps."

The color rushed back into Hans's cheeks.

"Oh, Herr Collin, nothing would please me more!" he cried.

Before many days had passed, he had made himself ready

and started on his way, bumping along in a rattletrap coach. At the border he climbed into a larger carriage, the six sturdy horses impatient to be off. Over the rocky roads and far out into the German countryside he jogged along, head thrust out of the window, his long fair hair blowing in the wind.

"It could be a fairy tale—the toy village yonder," he exclaimed. With bony finger he pointed to the tiny buildings, clinging like a wasp's nest to the mountain far above him.

Past racing waterfalls and deep canyons and through villages and cities he rode, crying out with joy at the quickly-changing scene.

The passengers smiled and nodded their heads. How the young stranger was enjoying their country. Opening their well-stocked lunch baskets, they shared hearty meals with him of fat sausage-rolls and black bread and bright sugared cakes.

The six beautiful weeks were like a dream as Hans roamed wide-eyed over the fair land, drinking in the beauty that was everywhere.

With a long sigh it was ended, and back again in the Collins' living room, the family sat for hours on end, enjoying the tales of his adventures.

"Capture it all on paper!" Edward shook a playful finger at the story-teller. "Perhaps the book will earn enough to take you off again to other lands."

"Hark you, boy!" Father Collin broke in quickly. "It would take much more than that to go journeying very far." After thinking quietly for a moment, he went on. "Sometimes the government gives funds for travel to persons who are worthy."

Henry C Pitz

Hans sat up quickly. "Oh, Herr Collin, do you think that I could ever receive such a gift from the State?"

"That is difficult to say. Few prove themselves worthy. But when the new book is ready, it would do no harm to ask."

In the months that rolled along, Hans worked hard in putting down thoughts of his journey, and at last his GAY SILHOUETTES was finished. And well liked by the people it was, too.

It was time, now, to take himself to the palace! If only the King would grant his dearest wish, he would ask for nothing more, his whole life long. With a prayer on his lips, he dressed with great care one morning and walked briskly to the palace gardens.

But at the great building, towering high above him, his courage almost left him. There would be so many, far more worthy, waiting for help from the ruler. "It would do no harm to ask, Hans." Father Collin's words stole quietly into his mind, and going swiftly through the heavy doors, he sat down to wait. The minutes seemed like hours, but at last he heard his name sounding down the long hall.

"HANS CHRISTIAN ANDERSEN!"

In a vast, high-ceilinged room sat the King, reading solemnly at a great desk. At the sound of footsteps he raised his eyes and looked carefully at his visitor.

"Ah yes, so this is the writer, Andersen. And what is your business with me, young man?"

His chance had come! Taking a step forward, Hans swallowed hard and was startled at the sound of his own voice.

"Your Majesty, to travel is the dream of everyone who earns his living with the pen. I would be so happy if—if—"

"Yes, yes, I know." The King went on to finish. "You would like special funds for this purpose?"

Hans sighed, his eyes dark with eagerness.

"More than anything in all the world," he exclaimed, "so that someday my writing might bring honor to my native Denmark."

"Well spoken, Andersen. But I can give you no promise, because of many who are already waiting. Perhaps you will send a copy of your latest work to the committee, and the members will go into the matter some time in the future."

From under his arm, Hans took a small, neat package.

"You will forgive me, Your Majesty. I have brought it with me!"

As he placed the book on the table, the King smiled broadly.

"An honest soul, if ever I saw one, and the first to come prepared!" he chuckled.

Hans's cheeks burned as he sped away from the palace. No doubt he had ruined his chances forever! Six months of traveling all lost. Six months would have taken him far, and how many adventures he could have set down for others to enjoy.

Ah well, he would give Copenhagen a new play for the theater. With a heavy heart he settled himself at his desk and long weeks he worked away, forgetting everything but the task at hand. Daily visits to the Collins' and to Henrietta brought the same answer from Hans: "No news from the palace."

One morning, as he was finishing his simple breakfast of bread and coffee, a sharp knock on the door startled him. There stood a messenger in dark livery, a square envelope in his hand.

"From His Majesty, the King, sir."

The answer had come! With trembling fingers Hans broke the heavy seal and the words danced before his eyes. With a great cry, he fell to the bed and buried his face in the pillow.

"Thank you, God! I thank You with all my heart," he murmured.

Such rejoicing as there was among his friends throughout all Copenhagen!

"Two whole years of traveling! What luck, Hans! A miracle!"

Storing away his belongings, Hans was soon ready for the great adventure. Through the city he visited for the last time all who had been so kind to him. Laden with their gifts, he made his way down to the waterfront where all the Collins, big and little, stood on the wharf to see him off.

"Good-by! Good-by! We will miss you sorely! Send us news of you!"

With whistles blowing, the sturdy ship nosed slowly out to sea. Hans stood at the railing, waving a great square of handkerchief until he could no longer see the dear faces of those he loved so well.

Two long years away. The blue light deepened into night and he felt suddenly alone under the dark bowl of heaven, the surging waters pounding in his ears.

"Herr Andersen, the postman is at your door." There stood the smiling captain at his elbow, a letter in his hand.

With a glad cry, Hans tore off the envelope and read eagerly the calm message of his good friend, Edward. And comforting letters came throughout the days, brought him by the faithful master of the ship. How carefully the good friends had planned their little surprises.

The gay city of Paris at last! And there were his jolly comrades of university days, waiting to greet him.

"Welcome to the capital of France! Such adventures as we have planned for you, Hans. No time to be wasted, not even for sleeping, my boy."

Paris in the springtime! Hans could not see enough of the beautiful city. In free moments his pen raced over the paper, telling his dear ones in Copenhagen of the glory of the music at the Opera House, plays at the theaters, his meetings with the great writers, Victor Hugo and Heine, and the composer, Cherubini, who sat at the piano with a cat on each shoulder.

At the end of the little visits, Hans drew from his pocket an old worn notebook.

"You will write a short line, if you please?" he would beg the notable. "Just a word for your poet friend Andersen, of Denmark."

On to Switzerland went the traveler, exclaiming in wonder at the ice-capped peaks, gleaming like silver in the sunshine.

High into the Jura mountain passes he jogged, winding in and out of the dark green pines. Rapidly now, they were coming to Le Locle, pretty town of watchmakers, where he would find the relatives of his good Danish friends.

Colder and colder it grew as they wound still higher into the mountains. The old driver smiled and held out his pipe, his long whiskers blowing in the wind as he leaned toward the window.

"Puff or two will put new life into you, young feller," he called.

Hans shook his head and waved the pipe away.

"Lucky not to have a right good snowstorm up here before night sets in," the old driver rumbled on.

But even before the afternoon was spent, great sheets of white flakes swept over the passes, and Hans looked in wonder through the holes in the clouds. Far down below, tiny villages dotted the land, and the hot summer sun was ripening the heady stalks of grain in the fields.

Le Locle, city of clocks and watches, at last. His bones stiff with the cold, Hans stood at the door of a fine old wooden house.

"Herr Andersen!" Hearty clockmaker Houriet gripped his hands in welcome. "We received your letter, and you cannot think how eager we are to have news of our dear cousin Jürgensen, in your far-away Denmark."

How good it was to be in the cheery warmth of the open fires. And all around, in every nook and corner, watches and clocks of every size spoke in loud and soft voices.

"You make them all, sir?" In amazement Hans bent over tiny, jeweled faces, glowing up at him from glass cases.

"Ah yes, with many helpers," answered his host. "They have been my life, and the life of my forefathers for long, long years. You will see how they are made, during your stay with us."

Hans looked into the shining faces gathered around him. Aunt Rosalie and Aunt Lydia fluttered about with little cries of joy, patting the tall young man as if they had known him forever.

Frau Houriet bustled toward the guest, her plump hands outstretched.

"The room, it is ready now. Come!" she commanded, leading the way up the winding staircase.

"You are so kind to me," murmured Hans. "I will be happy to spend the night here."

Frau Houriet turned sharply. "The night? You will make your home with us for as long as you care to stay. No more words, Herr Andersen!"

But little did she know how merry her household would turn out to be. In a very few days, all the neighbor children seemed to know that "Uncle Hans" had come to be with them.

Off into the mountains they took him at once, little packets of crusty bread and hunks of cheese clasped tightly in small hands.

"A race!" Hans sprang ahead of them, and climbing a stout boulder, called down to his puzzled little followers, "Find me if you can!"

"If you can—you can—can!" The echo darted in all directions, coming back swiftly from the mountain passes.

With shouts they found him at last, and pouncing on him, beat him with their small fists.

Happy games they played through the sunny hours. But best of all was the time when they sat to nibble lunches at midday, scrambling for a place close to their adored leader.

"Animals, Hans! The zoo!" they cried, eager eyes on his face.

Creature calls came at once from the large, cupped hands as lions and tigers, zebras and elephants spoke with their young. The tiny whimpers of baby elephants came echoing after them. And so real were they that the children cried out in alarm, fearing the little ones were lost forever from their mothers.

"Hans! Hans! Bring them back again!" they begged. And then the joyous gathering together of all the animals made the children clap their hands and shout for joy.

Home they went through the long shadows as the village bells rang out their peaceful evening song.

Never was Hans happier than in his new home with his friends. As the bright weeks grew into months, they would not hear of his leaving them.

Alone in his snug little room overlooking shaggy, ice-crowned peaks, he let his pen wander over the paper. At last his long poem, "Agnete" was finished, and with joyous heart one September morning he sent it on its way to his beloved homeland to be printed.

It was time to leave now, and sadly he packed his old leather trunk. The next day as he stood with his friends gathered around him, he was startled at the sound of weeping.

"Gr -r-r!" he growled fiercely, pouncing down on the children hiding their faces in his coat. "Smiles now, or I shall gobble you up in three big mouthfuls!"

Aunt Rosalie and Aunt Lydia drew from their pockets bright red circlets of yarn they had knitted in secret.

"To keep your wrists warm when you journey through the mountains," they explained, wiping their eyes.

Putting them on over his heavy coatsleeves, Hans danced about merrily, the bright wristlets spinning in red circles as his arms flew around him. In the hearty laughter he was gone, rumbling off in the coach.

"Good-by! Good-by!" he called, waving from the window as long as he could see the dear faces behind him. If only he could have taken the good friends with him on his journey into Italy, how happy he would have been.

Carefully the coach crept down the frozen roadway, the icy peaks overhead shining in clearest green against the blue sky. Shepherd boys, shivering in their vests of cowhide in the raw wind, watched as the wheels slipped and slid along the narrow pass. Down, down, down. In a few short hours, Hans breathed the sweet summer air and felt the warm Italian sun smile upon him.

"Italy! Italy!" he cried aloud. "I am in Italy at last!"

How many years he had read and talked and dreamed of this land of bright color and happy, singing people. In awe he visited her vast churches, and to her fine museums his eager steps took him, to wander on tiptoe to the great works of her sculptors and painters.

Learning that Thorwaldsen, the noted Danish sculptor, was in the old city of Rome, he went to his house to pay him a little visit. How good it would be to speak with his own countryman.

"Andersen? Ah yes, yes. I have read your works many times, and with pride," said the artist. Taking his visitor by the arm, he led him into the bright workroom. "Strange that we Danes should meet for the first time in a country outside our own."

Hans smiled brightly. "You will not remember it, sir, but our paths crossed in Copenhagen, long years ago. One day, as a homeless boy tramping the street, I chanced to meet you, the celebrated citizen of the city. Off came my battered hat and I bowed low as you passed by. Back you came and looked searchingly into my face. 'It seems that we have met before,' you said. 'Ah no,' I replied quickly. 'But I will remember you when I, too, am a great man some day!'"

Thorwaldsen's laughter rumbled in his throat as he put his arm around Hans's shoulders.

"So you see, we have been waiting to be good friends. You must promise me that you will come every day, to make up for lost time."

THORVALDSEN

Hans left the house, his heart singing for joy. One of the greatest men of all Denmark had asked to be his friend!

A good thing that he and three of his countrymen would spend the Christmas holidays not too far away from the home of the master, thought Hans. Just outside Rome they had found an old house where they would celebrate together. In high spirits, they soon moved in their belongings.

"A Yule tree! Above all else we must have a Christmas tree," cried Jensen, well-known painter of flowers.

"And plenty of garlands for decorating," added the artist, Christensen.

Hans peeled off his coat and rolled up his sleeves.

"Forward, gentlemen!" he commanded. "To work!"

Out into the garden he led them, and at once their nimble fingers were busily picking greens and fashioning them into wreathes and chains. Suddenly Hans stopped short, his eyes on an orange tree with bright fruit shining in the sun.

"The Christmas tree!" he shouted. With merry cries, the three leveled it to the ground and bore it, singing, to its new home. And a fine Yule tree it turned out to be, standing proudly in the great hall, decorated with its own golden balls.

Such a busy time as there was in the old house, to be ready in time for more Danish countrymen who would soon be at their door. At last all was in order, and with hearty greetings, the guests arrived for the festival. In and out of the rooms Hans led them in a gay procession, ending with a dance around the Christmas tree.

And then to the groaning table they took themselves, to feast to their heart's content. Hans smiled happily as he sat near his famous countryman, Thorwaldsen. From beneath the table he took the beautiful garland that he had worked so long to make, and leaving his chair, placed it before the great master, reciting a little poem that he had just written.

"Bravo, Thorwaldsen! Cheers for our countryman!" the cries went round the table.

What a merry evening there was, with songs and speeches and stories lasting far into the Christmas night. At last a hush fell over the company as Hans arose to face his companions.

"I should like to read you parts of my latest poem, 'Agnete,'" said he, quietly.

There was not a sound in the room but his low voice as it rose and fell in the beautiful lines. On and on he read, and when he had finished, he looked quickly at Thorwaldsen, who sat with great head bowed on his breast.

"So! So!" The famous Dane raised his eyes slowly. "It is a good work, Andersen. Your poem could have come from only one place in the world: our beloved Denmark." He sighed again. "How homesick you have made me for my native land. I could almost smell the green woods and hear the lapping of the waters against her shores."

A sudden stir at the door told everyone that the great moment of the evening had come. The rare prize was to bestowed on the most deserving member of the little group.

Hans leaned forward in his chair, ready and eager to applaud the winner.

Into the room marched two men, carrying a handsome silver cup that shone brightly in the candlelight.

"We are happy to present this remembrance of our Christmas together in Rome, to one of the friends gathered here," the first bearer announced.

His companion stepped forward, lifting high the beautiful treasure.

"To our countryman, Hans Christian Andersen!" he exclaimed amid ringing cheers.

Surely it was all a dream! Gripping the table, Hans tried to speak, but his words were drowned out in the shouting.

"Bravo, Andersen! Andersen! Andersen!" the cries rang through the old house.

Blinking away his tears, Hans read the words cut deep into the silver: "Christmas In Rome."

Never again would there be a festival as joyous as this. With loving care he wrapped the beautiful cup in a soft piece of old wool and put it safely away in his battered trunk.

Down to Naples he went, to watch the rumbling volcano spewing streams of fiery lava from her angry throat. But often now, as he journeyed here and there, the words of Thorwaldsen came into his mind: "I am homesick for my native land."

Ah yes, that was it. Little Denmark was calling him home, home to the land where he would smell again the green woods and hear the lapping of the waters against the shore.

Two years away was a long, long time. Would Copenhagen and the dear friends be the same as when he left them, he wondered.

CHAPTER SIX

"LONGLEGS! Ho, there, Longlegs!" The ragged boys of the canal called after the tall man with the mighty stride, his long arms swinging and head bent into the wind. Their friend was home again!

Hans turned and waved a greeting and in a flash the urchins were at his side, grimy hands outstretched.

"Robbers!" he scowled at them fiercely. "You would take away the last coin?" A sudden smile set them leaping and shouting about him. "Ah well, come with me, noisy rascals. You shall have your breakfast."

Laughing and tugging, they pulled him to the baker's.

"White Hat, kindly see that these sparrows have a good supply of crumbs today, if you please."

With a smile he was gone and soon found himself climbing the stairs to his room. "Bless me," he panted, turning the key in the lock, "I believe I am hungry, myself."

Munching away on a piece of bread, he sat at his desk.

"To work, you lazy fellow," he scolded himself. "Pennies to be earned, or no meat in the pot."

He must start his new book, telling of his adventures in Italy. But try as he would, no words went down on the white sheets before him. Ah well, no need to worry. Tomorrow would be a better day. Or perhaps a brisk walk along the canal would sharpen his wits.

Winding a gay woolen scarf around his neck, he started for the door when a thought made him pause. Taking his pen, he began to write, chuckling as the words scurried along.

What would old Bestimor think if she could see him now, setting down the tales she had told him when he begged for stories so long, long ago? Of course he would change them a little to suit his fancy.

"Hm! Hm! Hm!" he rumbled. "Four already finished, and so soon! And fun it was, in the bargain." He spread them out before him: The Real Princess, Big Claus and Little Claus, The Tinder Box, and Little Ida's Flowers.

Now to try them out on the children. He smiled at the thought, and hearing the rain beat down on the roof outside, slipped into his galoshes and was gone.

"Uncle Hans! Uncle Hans!" Eager young arms drew him inside the warm Collin nursery. "You promised a whole bagful of stories to make up for the long time you were away."

"Oho, so I did. Very well, my mousekins, you shall have some shiny new ones this very minute."

With shrill cries they scurried around him. Young Jonna was already on his lap, her legs dangling over his knees. Snuggling her head into the broad shoulder, she sighed. Now she was safe, where nothing in the whole world could harm her.

Hans held up a warning finger.

"Sh! Ready for the story. Anyone who makes even the tiniest noise will be turned into a fat green goat."

His eyes closed to narrow slits and his long, lean face was kind and gentle in the glow of the firelight as he began the tale of

THE REAL PRINCESS

"Once upon a time there was a prince who longed for a princess, a real princess for his very own. Many princesses there were to be had, simply for the asking. But a real princess would be hard to find. Right around the world he traveled, searching everywhere, but there was always something wrong. Never could he discover if the princesses were real. So home he came to the old king and queen, sad, indeed, for he did want a real princess so badly.

One evening there was a terrible storm. It thundered and lightninged and the rain came down in torrents. My, what a fearful night it was.

Right in the middle of the storm, someone knocked at the palace gate. Knock, knock, knock. "I'll go and open it myself," said the old king. And open the gate he did.

Who should be standing there but a princess. And a dreadful state she was in, from the rain and the storm and the wind. The water

streamed out of her hair, and water streamed out of her clothes. It ran in at the tops of her shoes and ran out again at the heel. But she said she was a real princess.

"Aha," said the old queen to herself. "We shall soon see if what she says is true."

She went into the bedroom and took all the bedclothes off the bed. Then very gently she laid a pea in the middle of the bedstead. Carefully she piled twenty mattresses on top of the pea. Then more carefully she piled twenty feather beds on top of the mattresses.

Now it was time for the princess to go to sleep, and she laid herself down on the twenty mattresses and the twenty feather beds. And not a sound was there until morning.

"How did you sleep, fair lady?" asked the king and the queen and the prince.

"Oh badly, badly," answered the princess. "Hardly have I closed my eyes the whole night long. I can not think what must have been in the bed. It was hard, very hard. Lack-a-day, I am black and blue all over."

Now the king and the queen and the prince saw at once that she must be a real princess. Nobody else would have felt a pea through twenty mattresses and twenty feather beds. Surely nobody but a princess could have such a delicate skin.

So the prince took her for his wife, now that he had found a real princess. Happy he was, indeed. And the pea was put into the Museum, where you may see it to this day, if someone has not stolen it away."

The clapping of small hands and loud cries echoed through the nursery as Hans's tale came to an end.

"Stories! Stories! More Stories!" Young arms pinned him to the chair as he started to rise.

With a merry laugh, Hans shook himself free. "Next week you shall have even better ones, my lambkins. But my coach and six are awaiting me just outside, so I must be off."

He strode to the hallway and stopped short, his long finger pointing to the line of small rubber boots beside his own.

"Beelzibub!" he exclaimed. "My galoshes have had little ones!"

To his great surprise, the tiny book of fairy tales spread like magic, to be read far and wide by the children of Denmark. And everyone was calling for more! Hans chuckled. They might even bring him greater success than his works for grownups!

He was so pleased with the funds that came from them that he decided to move into new quarters. This time he would have two rooms instead of one. Humming a lively tune, he pulled a box from under the bed and dumped in his belongings. Little enough there was to carry away.

What a joyous evening it was when he looked over the harbor from his new home for the first time! There were the drowsy black ships moving in the dark waters, their tall masts pointing sharply into the star-filled sky.

Sighing happily, Hans wrapped himself in his fine new flowered-silk dressing gown and tucked his toes into soft leather slippers. All the way from the city of Paris the beautiful gifts had just come with a little note:

"Allow me to send you this small token with my thanks, Herr Andersen, for the pleasure your books have given me.

From a very grateful friend."

Fine clothes were good to have. Hans sat dreaming before the glowing fire, his fingers moving lightly over the soft silk. He smiled as he thought of the funny old emperor who had cared a deal too much about clothes. How long it had been since he had thought of Bestimor's tale! Turning to his small table, he quietly wrote it down.

THE EMPEROR'S NEW CLOTHES

Long, long ago there lived an Emperor who was so fond of clothes that every penny he had went into coats to put on his vain back. Not a fig did he care about his soldiers nor the theater. Not even did he like to go riding in his carriage for an airing, unless it was to show off his fine costumes. A new coat there was for every hour of the day, and instead of saying, "The Emperor is in his council chamber," one had always to remember that he was in his dressing room.

One fine day, two strangers came to the kingdom. They said they were weavers and a great to-do they made over the rare colors and beautiful patterns in their magnificent cloth. Above all, clothes worn of such material had a magic power. Invisible they were, and anyone wearing them would know at once who was not fit for his office, or who was very stupid.

The Emperor said to himself, "That is just the material for me. I shall be able to tell the wise men from the fools." At once he had two looms set up and paid the weavers a great sum of money to start on the rare cloth. Bundles of purest silk and gold thread were sent with all haste to the workroom. But what did those rogue weavers do but hide it away in their traveling bags in the twinkling of an eye!

All day long they pretended to work at their looms, their arms moving in and out. But not a speck of cloth was there to be seen. So impatient was the Emperor to know how the wonderful material was growing, that he sent his honest old minister to discover the truth of the matter.

Bless me! thought the minister as he surveyed the empty looms. Am I a fool that I cannot see the cloth? Or still worse, I must be unfit for my position! But no one must know.

The weavers smiled upon him. "Is not the pattern the loveliest you have ever looked upon?" they asked. "And did you ever see such glowing colors?"

The poor minister could not take his eyes from the looms that were quite bare. "To be sure," he agreed. "No lovelier to be found in all the kingdom." Back to the Emperor he went with the news that no rarer cloth was to be found in the whole wide world.

The ruler was so pleased that more and more pure silk and gold thread and larger sums of money he sent to the weavers. And another official of his kingdom he sent to see how the work was getting on.

Like the first old minister, the official stared and stared at the bare looms and said to himself, "I have gone quite mad. Horrible! I am unfit for my office, but no one must know." Back to the ruler he went. "I could not take my eyes from the cloth," said he. "It is far beyond my power to describe."

Now everyone in the kingdom was talking of the treasured cloth. "I must go and see it for myself, while it is still on the looms," said the Emperor. So off he went with his band of followers and his two trusted officials. When he arrived, he found the two weavers busily at work, their arms moving this way and that, with not a single thread in their hands.

"Is it not magnificent, Your Majesty?" asked the two officials who had already visited the workrooms. "Such a graceful pattern, and colors glowing like jewels! No ruler in the world will have such fine clothes."

The Emperor could not believe his senses. How terrible, he thought. There is nothing here! I may even be unfit to be the ruler of my people! But not a soul must know. Aloud he said, "Rare beyond price. A wonderful piece of cloth, if ever I saw one."

"Splendid! Beautiful!" echoed the courtiers. "You must wear the clothes in the grand procession, Your Majesty." To each of the workmen the Emperor gave a cross to wear in his buttonhole and bestowed on them the special title of "Sir Weaver."

The day of the procession drew near and the workmen sat up all night, burning more than sixteen candles to finish the material in time. With great scissors they slashed through the air, pretending to cut the clothes to measure. Then to the workroom came the Emperor and the members of his court for the fitting.

"We can tell better how the clothes will look if the Emperor will first remove his own garments," said the weavers. "Ah yes, now we put on the new trousers. What a perfect fit! Here is the coat and mantle, and last of all, the long train." With great care they pretended to help him into the new clothes. "Like a spider's web," they murmured. "The material so fine that one would think he had nothing on."

"To be sure. Exactly," agreed the band of noblemen. Of course they could see nothing at all, for there was nothing to be seen.

"It is time for the grand procession to begin," announced the head minister. "The canopy awaits His Majesty."

Down the street and through the town walked the ruler proudly, admired on all sides by the people crowding the roadway. "See the Emperor's new clothes and his long train!" they cried. "Was there ever a sight so magnificent?" Of course no one would say that he could see nothing, and prove himself unfit for his position, or a fool.

"But the Emperor hasn't anything on!" said a little child. His father laughed. "Pay no attention to his foolish talk," said he.

Now the Emperor heard the child and a shiver ran from his head to his toes. "But the procession must go on," said he to himself. So he held himself more proudly still and walked on through the town in the clothes that were not there at all.

Hans smiled. The story was finished at last. He could almost hear the children scolding, "But that's only one, Uncle Hans!" And he would say, "Why, so it is, my pretty dears. I might have known there would need to be two, just for company."

His pen began to scratch again. This time he would tell them Bestimor's tale of the little tin soldier.

THE STEADFAST TIN SOLDIER

Once there were five and twenty little tin soldiers. All brothers they were and looked exactly alike, since they had been made from the same old tin spoon. Their eyes they kept well to the front, and smart, indeed, they were in shining red and blue uniforms, muskets held firmly over their shoulders.

The very first word they heard in all this world was "Soldiers!" A little boy clapped and shouted his joy at so fine a birthday present and began to line them up on the table. But when he came to the very last member of the regiment, he cried out, "This one is different. He has only one leg!"

Sad, but true. The tin had run out before he was quite finished. But he stood just as staunchly on one leg as the others on two. And what adventures he was to have, this little soldier with only one leg.

On the table behind him was a splendid cardboard castle with trees in front and a little mirror lake with waxen swans swimming upon it. But most beautiful of all was a lovely maiden standing in the doorway. Cut out of paper she was, and her dress was like palest cloud mist. A delicate blue ribbon crossed her breast and held a bright silver spangle as big as her face. Ah, how beautiful she was!

The heart of the little tin soldier beat fast as he looked at her, standing there with her two arms outstretched toward him. Like a ballet dancer she was poised on one toe, the other leg held so far behind her that the soldier couldn't see it at all. She must have only one leg, just like himself!

"That would be just the wife for me!" said he to himself. "But she is much too grand, living in a palace. Ah well, at least I can make her acquaintance." But he must wait his chance. So behind the snuff box he lay as still as a mouse, where he could admire the lovely creature to his heart's content.

Night settled down and when everyone in the house had gone to bed, out scampered the toys for a frolic. Battles there were and fine balls, with the nutcracker turning somersaults and the slate pencil scratching out jokes on the slate. Such a to-do there was that the canary woke with a start and gave everyone a lecture in rhyme.

In all the frolicking, the tin soldier never once took his eyes from the little dancer. And without moving, the dainty maiden held out her arms to him, poised like a fairy thing on her pointed toe.

Then on the very stroke of twelve, pop! went the lid of the snuff box and out bounced a fierce black goblin.

"Tin soldier, please to keep your eyes to yourself!" he commanded sternly. But when the little man pretended not to hear, the goblin became angrier than ever. "Just wait until tomorrow, and see what will happen!" he shouted.

Poor little soldier. The very next morning, when he was put on the window ledge, up went the window and out he fell. Down, down, down. Three whole stories he dropped and landed right on his head. There he was, stuck fast between the stones, his one leg straight up in the air.

Suddenly the rain began to come down in torrents. Whole bucketfuls were all around him when along came two street urchins. "A tin soldier!" they cried, pulling him loose. "Let's send him sailing!"

A newspaper boat was made in a trice and throwing him into it, they sent him whirling along in the rushing water.

But straight and steadfast stood the little soldier, gripping his musket as he spun dizzily and pitched this way and that in the tossing boat. Suddenly he shot under the gutter, far down in a deep dark tunnel.

"Where am I going now?" he said to himself. "Oh dear, it must be the curse of that black goblin. If only the little lady were with me, I shouldn't mind at all even if it were twice as black."

At that very minute, out in front of him jumped a great water rat. "Your pass. Hand it over!" he shouted. The little tin soldier looked neither to right nor left and clutched his musket tighter than ever as the boat swept him on. "Stop him! He hasn't shown his pass! He hasn't paid his toll!" screamed the water rat, swimming after the boat and gnashing his teeth in rage.

Through the tunnel and out into the light swept the boat, right toward the deep, dangerous canal. Into a swift whirlpool it swung round and filled to the top, right up to the very neck of the poor little soldier. Down, down out of sight sank the boat. As the water rushed over his head, the tin soldier could think of nothing but the little dancer whom he would never see again.

At that very moment the paper gave way and the little soldier went right through the bottom of the boat, straight into the open jaws of a great big fish! Darker than a dungeon it was inside the creature, and cramped, besides. The little soldier lay as still as could be, not even so much as winking an eye. Then, before he had time to think, he was jerked about in a most frightening way as the big fish thrashed and fought in the water. At last he lay perfectly still.

"Now what is going to happen?" wondered the little soldier. Just then, something struck through like a flash of lightning, and to his amazement, he was in broad daylight. Someone was shouting in his ears, "A tin soldier!"

The big fish had been caught, taken to market, and brought to the kitchen where the cook had cut him through with a big knife. Up the stairs she carried the soldier and everyone gathered around to behold the wonderful man who had gone traveling in a fish's stomach. But the little soldier was not at all proud.

And then, wonder of wonders! When he was put on the table, he discovered that he was back in his old home! There were the same children and the same toys. Ah yes, and there was the same little dancer just where he had left her, arms outstretched, her eyes looking straight into his. Tin tears he could have shed at a sight so dear, but soldiers never weep.

As they gazed at each other without saying a word, a small boy snatched up the soldier and for no reason at all, threw him into the fire. There he stood in the terrible heat, high flames all around him and his bright color gone. But his eyes were still on the maiden, and hers were on him.

Suddenly a puff of wind sent her sailing across the room, right into the fire beside the little soldier. In an instant she was gone in the flames. Sighing, the steadfast tin soldier melted right down to a tiny lump. The next morning, in cleaning up the ashes, all that the servant found was a little tin heart and a wee spangle, burned as black as a coal.

There must be food each day, and funds to pay for his room, and fairy tales alone would not do that for him. And so Hans began not one, but two new books for the people of Denmark and Sweden to read.

One dark winter's morning, with the wind howling down the chimney, he was hard at work when a sudden, sharp knocking stopped his scribbling. Opening the door, he discovered a tall, handsomely dressed stranger bowing to him.

"Andersen, the poet! May I come in?" The visitor shook hands warmly and seated himself beside the fireplace. "Long I have been waiting to add my praises to those of my countrymen for the splendid work you have given to Denmark," said he, his eyes glancing around the clean little room as he spoke.

"Thank you, sir. There is little else that I could do in this world but put down the thoughts that grow in my mind," said Hans, simply. Closely he looked at the stranger. Who could he be, out visiting on such a frosty morning?

The two spoke long together and at last the stranger left. Closing the door swiftly, Hans picked up the small white card he had left behind. "Count Rantzan Britenburg, Prime Minister of Denmark," he read.

The Prime Minister in his simple little home! But what could he want? Throughout the days, Hans was puzzled, indeed. But he had not long to wait to discover the errand of his kind visitor.

One afternoon as he sat mending a tear in his coat, a messenger handed him a large envelope and hurried down the stairs.

"From the palace!" Hans exclaimed aloud. "What can be wrong?" Ah well, no need to worry. He would open it when he arrived at Henrietta's. Tucking it into his pocket, he dressed quickly and was off down the street. Arriving at the fine home of his friend, he forgot it at once in the warm fire-glow and the handsome table set with gleaming silver and crystal.

"My dear Hans, you are just in time to light the candles for tea." Laughingly Henrietta handed the long match to her good friend.

"The better to see these beautiful cakes," he declared, helping himself to the spiced dainties, fresh from the oven. As he feasted on the rich food, he looked again at the long tapers in the box. "Matches!" he murmured, a far-away look in his eyes.

Henrietta took the delicate cup from the big hands. "I feel a story in you, my friend. Nothing would please me more," she coaxed gently.

Hans leaned back in the comfortable chair before the bright fire and crossed his bony knees.

"As long as I can remember, it has been with me, this tale of the little match girl."

THE MATCH GIRL

It was a bitterly cold day and the very last of the old year. Snow was falling and in the gloom of early evening, a little girl was walking through the streets. Bareheaded she was, and there were no shoes on her feet. To be sure, she had started out in her mother's slippers. But so big were they that they had fallen from her feet when she darted across the road to escape the carriages.

Search as she would, one could not be found; the other was snatched from the mud by a mischievous boy. "A cradle for my children some day!" he laughed, running home with it under his arm.

The little girl walked on, her feet red with the cold, her soft, fair curls powdered with snow. A poor day it had been, without a single coin in her pocket. Her father was sure to beat her if she went home with unsold matches in her apron. Besides, it was cold there, with nothing but a roof overhead and the icy wind whistling through straw-filled cracks.

The windows of the houses were alight with good cheer as the small maiden crept along the street. Often she stopped to peer into warm, comfortable homes and sniff hungrily the roast goose, sizzling and browning in the oven.

New Year's Eve! How good it would feel to be warmed a little. Into a corner she crept, and sitting on the stones, drew her little feet under her. Surely it would do no harm to take just one match from the bundle. Carefully she drew it from the box and struck it sharply against the wall. Scr-r-atch, it burst into flame. Like a warm candle it glowed in the night as she held her little hands over it.

But how strange the light was, changing everything around her. It seemed that she was sitting before a big stove with shining brass nobs and big brass cover. The fire burned fiercely and the little girl stretched out her feet to warm them when suddenly all was darkness. The stove had vanished, and all that was left was the end of the match in her hand.

Just one more taper — only one. Quickly she set it afire and lo! the stone wall before her thinned to a delicate veil. Through it she could look right into a room with dinner table all set with snowy linen and shining silver. There sat a plump roast goose, stuffed to bursting with prunes and apples. Before her startled eyes, it jumped down from the table and with knife and fork still in its breast, waddled straight toward her.

Then the match went out and the goose was gone. All that her eyes could see was the thick stone wall. Quickly, quickly, another taper! In the bright radiance she found herself sitting under the most beautiful Christmas tree with thousands of candles burning on the the branches. How warm and bright they were! She stretched her arms up to them and when the match went out, found them still shining above her in the stars high over her head. And suddenly, one of the biggest stars fell through the sky, leaving a long train of fire behind it.

"Someone there is who dies," thought the little girl. Her kind grandmother, long since dead, had often told her that falling stars meant souls finding their way to God.

Another match scraped against the wall. There in the bright light stood her dear old granny, the only one who had really loved her in this world. With clear and shining face she smiled down at her little grandchild, the loveliest kind of smile.

"Take me with you, Grandmother!" cried the little girl. "Take me with you, so I will not be alone when the taper goes out!"

Scr-r-atch! Scr-r-atch! Scr-r-atch! The whole bundle of matches she swept against the stones to keep her dear grandmother with her. Never was there a brighter glow and never was her granny more beautiful. Bending down, she swept the little girl in her arms and together they flew up through the starry heavens. High above the earth they sailed in great joy, straight to the kingdom of God, where there was no cold and no hunger.

The next day, when the New Year's sun climbed into the sky, they found the little girl on the stones, leaning against the wall. Her cheeks were red and a smile lighted her face. In her small hands she held a bundle of matches, most of them burned to the very end.

"She was trying to warm herself," the people said. But little they knew of the beautiful things she had seen and how happily she went into the New Year with her beloved old granny.

Hans sighed as the story came to an end, and struggling to his feet, slipped into his overcoat. Why, there was the letter in his pocket!

"How forgetful I am!" he cried. "But now you shall share my news, good or bad, little Henrietta. From the palace it has just come to me."

Opening the envelope, he looked at the words and sank back in his chair, the paper falling to the floor.

"Surely this could never happen to me!" he gasped.

In an instant Henrietta was at her friend's side, picking up the letter.

"Oh Hans! Hans!" she cried, and read aloud the message from the King of Denmark:

> "FROM THIS DAY ON, HANS CHRISTIAN ANDERSEN, POET OF DENMARK, SHALL RECEIVE A SUM FROM THE STATE, SUFFICIENT FOR HIS DAILY NEEDS FOR AS LONG AS HE SHALL LIVE."

Never to worry again about a place to lay his head or food for the next meal! A great joy shone in his face as Hans bowed his head in thanks. His eyes were bright with tears when he looked up at his little companion.

"Oh, Henrietta, what a wonderful place the world is!" he cried. Pulling her from her chair, he danced with her to the door. "A party!" he laughed. "There must be a fine party to celebrate my good fortune. Away, lucky fellow, to make ready!"

A Christmas gathering there would be, and for the children, of course. But larger quarters he must have. The small hotel just across from the Royal Theater would be the very place to live, and early the next morning he took himself to the pompous manager.

"Two rooms, if you please," he ordered. "And perhaps—perhaps they could look out on the theater square?"

At the wistful tone, the manager was all smiles.

"To be sure, Herr Andersen, the best rooms in the hotel." With a deep bow, he led the way up the stairs.

Soon Hans was settled and the planning began. And not until Christmas day, itself, was all in order for the celebration, with the little tree in place and the presents neatly tied and piled beneath its branches.

"Oho, the Christmas star! To think that I should have forgotten it! The children would never have forgiven me." Hans set to work with his sharp scissors and in a very few minutes, the top of the little fir tree was crowned in gleaming silver. And just in time, with "Merry Christmas, Uncle Hans!" calling outside his door.

The jolliest party it was, indeed, with bright little faces gathered around the tiny, lighted tree. Hans was on his knees, his long arms darting here and there, filling eager hands with white packages. His laughter echoed with the shouting as small fingers unwrapped gay scarves and mittens and toys and sweetmeats, until there seemed no end.

Suddenly above the clamor, a loud weeping arose. In an instant the littlest guest was safe in Hans's arms.

"What! No gingerbread man?" He thrust a fat cake into the tiny hands. "There now, my rosebud," he soothed, rocking and patting the small creature clinging to him. "If you are as still as a cloverleaf, you shall have a story all your own."

"Me, too! Me, too!" With a shout the scrambling group was around his knees and Hans chuckled.

"Very well. Then you shall all share the tale of the little fir tree.

THE FIR TREE

Deep in the green wood stood a little fir tree. Such a pretty little tree it was, but most of the time, very unhappy. All around grew its tall comrades, and the little fir wanted to grow up fast, so that it could be as tall as they.

Plenty of fresh air there was, and sunlight, but not a thing did the little tree care about them. Not even did it care for the children who scampered about, picking berries, and came to it to rest.

"What a pretty little tree," they said. "It is the very littlest in all the woods."

Little, indeed! The fir bristled with anger and decided to grow with all its might. "Oh, to be as tall as my brothers," it sighed. "So that I could look out over the whole wide world and see what is going on."

The wind blew and the sun shone, and winter came to spread a soft white blanket around its feet. A tiny rabbit came hopping along, and hopped right over the little fir.

"If I were only tall enough, he could never do that!" thought the tree, crossly.

Two winters went by, and the little fir grew and grew until it had grown two whole joints. But how it trembled to see the wood-cutters chop into its tall brothers, sending them crashing to the ground. Where were they going now? It would ask the storks and the swallows when they came back to nest in the springtime.

"No one knows for sure," answered a thoughtful stork. "But I think I smelled fir when I flew by the tall masts of new ships on their way to Egypt. Yes, I believe they wanted to be remembered to you."

The little fir sighed. To grow tall enough to be a mast and travel on the high seas would be the most wonderful thing in the world.

The wind soughed through its branches and kissed the little tree, and the dew wept over it, because it was so young.

Christmas time came and the woodchoppers searched through the forest again, looking for trees to cut down.

The little fir quivered in all its branches when they tramped through the deep snow to look at it. They were going to take it at last! But when the ax struck deep into the trunk, it felt sick with pain and fell fainting to the ground.

Ah well, it would soon feel better. But instead of being happy, it was a bit sad to leave its dear comrades and the bushes and flowers, yes, even the little rabbit that had jumped right over its head.

Into town rode the fir on a big sleigh, and the first thing it knew, out came two servants and carried it into a fine drawing-room. How it trembled with joy as lovely young ladies hung golden balls and colored papers and walnuts and toys over all its branches. And on the very top of its head, a gold tinsel star shone forth.

How beautiful I am! Never did I dream of anything quite like this, thought the fir. Perhaps I shall take root and stand here both winter and summer in all my finery. If only the trees in the wood and the swallows and storks and sparrows, yes — even the little rabbit, could see me now.

Night time came and in rushed the children, crying out with joy at the splendid sight. Round and round the fir they danced and shouted, plucking every present from the branches. If the poor tree had not been held down firmly, it surely would have been pulled to the floor.

Soon the branches were bare. Not a single thing was left but the fine gold star at the top. Even now the children had forgotten the fir, until they pulled a fat little man to a chair beside it.

"Tell us a story!" they cried. "Tell us about *Humpty-Dumpty!*" And happy they were when *Humpty*, even though he tumbled downstairs, got right up again and married a princess.

The fir tree stood very still and listened. Not one of the birds in the forest had ever told a tale like this. What would they think if I tumbled down stairs and married a princess, it thought. Strange things can happen in this world.

The fir dreamed of the next day, when it would be as beautiful as ever. They would deck its branches again and put on fresh candles. But when morning dawned, in came the servants and whack! — down fell the tree with a terrible bang. Up the stairs it was dragged, far up to the attic and pushed back in a dark corner.

"How thoughtful of them," said the fir to itself. "They are only waiting for spring to come, when they can plant me again."

But it was very lonely, all by itself as the days went by. If only it could be back in the forest again with its friends, and feel the warm sun and the kind wind, how happy it would be.

Squeak! Squeak! A little mouse came out of his hole and sniffed at the branches. The fir was glad enough of any company and told its visitor again and again the only story it knew: *Humpty-Dumpty*. But the mouse grew tired of the same old tale and went back to the larder where he would dart in thin, and squeeze out fat.

The fir tree sighed and sighed with loneliness and dreamed of the forest until the springtime came.

Then one morning, what a stir there was in the dusty attic. Out came the fir, with the gold star still shining on its head, and down the stairs to the garden it was dragged. Ah, how good was the warm sun, and how beautiful the roses and the blossoming linden tree. Was there ever a sight so fair?

"Now I shall live again, for they will surely plant me deep in the earth," said the fir to itself as it tried to stretch out its branches. But alas, all withered it was, and brown, and a great sadness came over it. "My days are finished," wept the tree. "If only I had stayed in the forest!"

"See the gold star," shouted the children. Quickly they tore it from the top and ran away, laughing.

Out came a servant, and chopping the tree to bits, set fire to the pieces. A beautiful blaze there was, but the fir moaned and moaned, and each moan sounded with a loud sharp crack.

At the noise, the children laughed and shouted and danced about the flames, crying "Pif! Paf! Pif!" On down to the tiniest cinder burned the poor tree, thinking and dreaming of its beautiful days in the deep green forest that would never come again.

And so the little fir tree was no more.

How good life was for him now. Each morning, after his hair had been carefully curled at the barber's, Hans came back to his rooms to find a great pile of invitations awaiting him.

"Andersen!" He shook his finger at himself in the mirror. "Do you know what a lucky fellow you are?"

Dressed in his fine topcoat, all lined in velvet, and shiny silk hat crowning his graying locks, he set out with handsome walking stick to visit the noblest homes in all the countryside. Even to the palace he went, one bright afternoon, to read his new play to the King and Queen.

"We are proud of the honor that you have brought to your native country, my good Andersen," said the monarch, placing the rarest golden chain around the neck of his guest. "May your works grow in number as the links bound here together."

Hans looked down at the priceless treasure, its endless pieces of beaten gold locked in gleaming clusters.

"Your Majesty, I would need three lifetimes to accomplish such a task," he laughingly replied.

In the bright summer days, off to Danish castles in the cool green countryside rode Hans to spend happy weeks, entertaining his royal hosts and friends for hours with stories and poems and plays.

One evening, in the vast dining hall of the Danish Crown Prince, there was silence as the tall man at the head of the table raised his glass.

"A toast to our honored guest, Hans Christian Andersen," he declared, looking intently into the long, lean face of the writer of tales.

He must make a reply, and at once, thought Hans. All eyes were on him as his great frame unfolded itself slowly, towering like a giant over the table.

"Your Highness," he began, "I cannot help thinking of a day, many long years ago, when a poor boy from the village of Odense stood before you, singing his heart out and reciting his own poems and plays. The dearest wish of that cobbler's son was to become an actor."

The Crown Prince smiled in remembrance. "Ah yes, yes. I can see him now. And if I recall rightly, I advised him to be a carpenter, instead."

"You did, indeed," answered Hans quietly. "That young Odense boy was I."

A deep silence fell upon the company, broken at last by the Prince.

"What a loss to Denmark if the boy had followed my advice!" said he. "A new toast, my countrymen—a toast to the village boy of Odense!"

As the years rolled by, the sum from the State was even larger, and Hans took himself again and again to far-away countries that he loved so well. Wherever he went, his works were known and everyone hastened to do him homage.

Gifts and honors were heaped on him as he journeyed from one country to another. Kings and queens and noblemen invited him to their courts, presenting him with medals and precious jewels. Carefully they were tucked away in his old leather trunk, sometimes to be worn and sometimes to be sold, if extra funds were needed.

But as dearly as he loved to go traveling, Hans always waited impatiently for the boat to land safely again in little Denmark.

"Can you bear it, child?" he would say to a passenger, his long hands clasping and unclasping as he trod up and down the deck. "Thirteen whole minutes before we can set foot on the blessed shores of our beloved fatherland!"

More and more of his time he spent in writing wonder tales. And now that he had come to know and love the great Swedish singer, Jenny Lind, so well, he decided to write a little story about her. He would call it, THE NIGHTINGALE.

The gentle-hearted songstress sighed with delight when he read it to her for the first time. From then on, whenever she heard his step outside the door, she ran to open it, crying, "Come in, brother! Come in, and tell me my story, THE NIGHTINGALE!"

THE NIGHTINGALE

A great many years ago, there lived a Chinese Emperor in the most beautiful palace in all the world. Of costliest porcelain it was built, but so delicate that it could scarcely be touched at all. Around it was a garden filled with rarest flowers, the prettiest tied with little silver bells that tinkled merrily so they would be sure to be noticed.

Far down to the sea stretched the gardens, where the big boats sailed right beneath the branches of the trees in the wood. Now in this very wood there lived a nightingale with song so glorious that a fisherman, out to pull in his nets, could do no more work at all, for listening. "Ah, how beautiful!" he sighed, and wept.

Visitors from round the world who came to see the porcelain palace and the gardens, heard the song and declared, "This is the best of all!" Home they went, many to write books and poems of the wonders they had seen. "But the nightingale is the best of all," they wrote.

Now the Emperor, seated on his golden chair in the garden, nodded and smiled as he read such beautiful things about his kingdom. But when he came to the words, "The nightingale is the best of all," he sent at once for his Lord-in-Waiting.

"A rare bird, here in my own gardens, and I have never heard it sing!" he cried. "Go and fetch it at once. If it is not here by evening, everyone at court shall be punched in the stomach after dinner!"

Upstairs and downstairs and through the gardens ran the frightened Lord-in-Waiting and half the court in search of the nightingale, for no one wished to be punched in the stomach after dinner. But search as they would, the rare bird could not be found. At last the little kitchen maid declared that she knew it very well.

"Down by the sea it lives," said she. "And so beautiful is its song that tears come to my eyes and I feel as if my dear mother were kissing me."

"Take me to him at once, and you shall have the honor of standing behind the door and watching the Emperor eat his dinner," said the Lord-in-Waiting.

As the little kitchen maid led the group through the woods, a loud mooing and croaking began. "Ah, how beautiful! Ravishing! Like the tinkling of silver bells!" exclaimed the courtiers. "Oh, no, that is only a cow and some frogs," explained the kitchen girl. Just then the nightingale began to sing. "Only listen!" she cried. "There he sits on yonder tree!"

"A bird so humble with so rare a song!" said the Lord-in-Waiting, gazing up at the tiny creature in dress of somber grey. In loud tones he called, "Dear nightingale, the Emperor requests your presence in the palace this evening to entertain him with your singing."

"With pleasure," answered the little bird, bursting into rapturous song. "He is sure to be a great success at court," decided the Lord-in-Waiting, and everyone echoed his words.

And a great success he was, trilling on a special golden perch until the tears rolled down the Emperor's cheeks and every heart was touched. The ladies were so pleased, they filled their mouths with water, trying to gurgle like the nightingale when anyone spoke to them. Indeed, the whole town talked of nothing but the little bird, and one had only to say "Night" for the other to say "Gale" when they met on the street.

One day at the palace, a package arrived for the Emperor, marked "NIGHTINGALE." "Another book about my little feathered friend," said he. But what should he find but the most beautiful artificial bird. Exactly like the real nightingale it was, but far more handsome, covered from tip to toe with diamonds and rubies and sapphires. Wound up, it sang one of the nightingale's own songs, flipping its gold and silver tail in a delightful manner.

"Far better than the real nightingale," declared the court, after the two birds had sung a duet together, which did not go too well. "The live one from the forest just sings whatever comes into his head, which is no good at all."

The poor little nightingale's heart was quite broken, and away he flew, back to his home in the green forest by the sea. "Ungrateful wretch!" scolded the courtiers, and the bird was banished from the kingdom.

For a whole year the artificial bird delighted the court with his same song. Even the street urchins knew it by heart. "Zizizi" and "Cluck-cluck-cluck" they sang. And the Emperor practiced until he could sing it, too.

Then one night, while the bird was singing the ruler to sleep, a dreadful thing happened. WHIZ – Z – Z-zzzzzz, rattled the wheels with a horrible sound and the song stopped right in the middle. Up jumped the Emperor from his bed and called the Master Physician at once. But nothing could he do. Then the clockmaker rushed into the bedchamber with all haste and patched up the insides of the little creature. But so delicate and worn out was the bird that only once a year could it be played from that time on.

This was a terrible blow to the poor Emperor and to everyone at court. Five sad years passed by and one day the ruler became very ill. Still and pale he lay in the great bed behind the velvet curtains. Everyone thought him dead and the servants ran off to hold coffee parties to celebrate so great an occasion.

But the Emperor was still alive. If only the little bird would sing, he knew he would get well again. "Sing! Sing!" he breathed. But the artificial creature just sat on his silken cushion in the moonlight, all his jewels glittering. "Sing! Sing!" begged the Emperor with the last strength that was in him.

Suddenly the loveliest song came floating through the open window. There sat the real little nightingale, who had heard of the illness of the ruler and had come to bring him comfort and hope.

The blood began to flow faster through the Emperor's body and he smiled. "Oh, thank you, little bird. You have sung death away from my heart. You must never leave me again," said he. "Everything that I have is yours."

"Your heart I love far better than your crown," sang the little bird. "But I cannot live in a palace, for my song sounds better in the greenwood. Often I will come to your window and tell you of the good and evil in the hearts of men. This I will do on your promise that never will you say to anyone, 'A little bird gave me the news.' "

Away he flew, far away to his home in the forest by the sea. And the servants crept into the bedchamber to look after their dead Emperor. Up he sat and wished them all a "Good-day."

One morning, finishing his simple breakfast of porridge just as the sun slipped over the high windowsill, Hans called a cheery good-day to the boy who came to pack his small bag.

"The grey trousers and blue waistcoat, if you please, and plenty of clean linen," he directed. "Two pairs of boots will do for tramping. Think of it, lad, three beautiful weeks to roam as I choose on the vast estate of Gisselfeldt!"

Humming at the happy thought, he carefully locked away his papers in an old cupboard, and patting his freshly-curled hair into place, was ready to leave.

"See that the rooms are dusted each day that I am gone," he warned, "and polish the floors until the light glows in them." Hans put an arm around the young shoulders. "I shall teach you as my good mother taught me when I was a lad. Mor! Dear Mor! If only she were alive to enjoy the good life with her son!"

Out on the beautiful estate, not too far from Copenhagen, he wandered through the wide-spreading parks to his heart's content. Wild deer scampered through the brush at the sound of his footsteps, stopping to drink from a small blue lake.

Hans raised his face to the healing sun and sighed with contentment. How peaceful it was, and close to heaven, itself. Walking on through a gentle little glade, he came upon a sight so beautiful as to make him cry aloud.

On a little round pond, fringed in delicate lacy ferns, floated ten noble, pure-white swans. Without rippling the water they drifted here and there, graceful long necks curved proudly over their snowy bodies. Hans could not take his eyes from the fairy picture.

Henry C Pitz

He seated himself on the bank and peered through the ferns to feast long on the beauty and loveliness of a sight so fair. As he watched the white birds, dazzling on their sunlit pool, thoughts kept coming into his mind that would not be put out.

Had he, Hans Christian, always been a swan, hatched by accident in a duckyard? Had he been the ugly duckling in the brood? Over and over the thoughts turned in his head until they began to weave themselves into a story of his own life.

He could not wait to get back to the house for fear the tale would be lost. Out came his trusty pad from his pocket, and THE UGLY DUCKLING, was scribbled on his bony knees.

THE UGLY DUCKLING

It was summer in the country, and very beautiful, indeed. On the bright green meadows the stork stalked about on his red legs, jabbering in Egyptian, the language his mother had taught him.

Dreaming near him in the field was an old manor house, with a deep moat built all around it. And thick as could be, burdock leaves grew at the edge of the water until they looked almost like a wood. There, hidden safely away, a duck sat on her nest, sighing with weariness. If only the ducklings would hatch! At last, one day, the eggshells began to crack.

"Peep, peep! Peep, peep!" The baby ducks poked out their heads to see what was going on in the big green world. Their mother was glad to have them look, because green is good for the eyes.

She shook herself and was about to get up, when she discovered the biggest egg of all, still unhatched. An old duck coming to call, peered into the nest.

"It's a turkey egg, you can be sure," said she. "And plenty of trouble it will give you. Plenty, my dear."

At last the egg cracked, and what a big ugly baby tumbled out! His mother took a good look at him, turning her head this way and that. He isn't like the others, not a single speck, she thought. Perhaps he is a turkey baby, after all. Ah well, we shall find out, soon enough.

Down to the moat she took her brood. "Quack, quack," said she. Into the water they plunged after her and the ugly, big gray one swam along just like the rest.

"There is no turkey in that child," said the mother duck. "He is my very own son, and not too horrible to look at, if you know just how to look at him."

Into the duckyard she led her children to call on all the creatures. "Keep close to me so that you won't get stepped on, and be sure to mind the cat!" she warned, bustling on ahead. "Bend your heads to that old duck yonder with a red rag around her leg. Spanish blood she has in her, and that makes her a very fine lady. Watch your manners, and be sure to turn your toes out, like well-bred ducks should do. Now bend your necks and say 'Quack!'"

The other ducks looked at the new brood. "How strange the big ugly one is," they said. "We cannot have him around. Better give him a good whacking." And they did.

The old lady with the Spanish blood held her head high. "Nice children you have there, all but the ugly gray one," said she.

"Too long in the shell," explained his mother. "That's why he is so large. But he swims as well, even a little better, than the others. So he is sure to amount to something in the world."

The new ducks were quite at home now, all but the last one out of the shell. Everywhere he was pecked and pushed and laughed at. And the big turkey gobbler scared him almost out of his wits, rushing at him and gobbling until he was red in the face. Even his family was unkind to him and wished he had never been born.

So he ran away to the marsh where the wild ducks lived. "Who are you?" they asked. "My, how ugly you are! But it is all right if you don't marry into our family."

Bang! Bang! The guns of the hunters brought down the very creatures who had just spoken to him! Shivering with fright, the little duckling lay hidden among the reeds. Then splash! on through the water came the bird dog, straight to the little duckling. His eyes glared and his jaws were wide open. With a great splash he went on, never touching the little feathered creature.

"I was too ugly," gasped the duckling. "So ugly that the dog wouldn't even bite me."

When darkness came he crept from the marsh and began to run. Faster and faster he went over the fields until he ran right into a great storm. The wind blew harder and harder, pushing him this way and that, until he found himself at the door of a poor little hut. There was just room to squeeze through a crack, and in a minute he was safely inside.

There, in the tiny room lived an old woman with her cat and her hen. Now the woman could not see too well. "What luck for me," said she, looking at the stranger. "Soon I shall have duck eggs." But after three long weeks, there was not even one to be found.

"Can't you lay eggs?" asked the hen.

"No, because I'm a drake," answered the duckling.

"Then please to hold your tongue," said the hen.

"Can you purr, arch your back, and make sparks?" asked the cat.

"No, that I cannot," answered the duckling sadly.

"Then be still when others are talking," said the cat.

This was no place for him, thought the duckling. He must find a pond to swim in. So off he went to live in the water. But still there was no peace. Everyone was unkind to him because he was so ugly.

Autumn came, and one evening a flock of handsome birds came out of the reeds. Enormous swans they were, and dazzling white, with long graceful necks. Flapping their great wings, they flew high into the heavens to search for warmer climes.

The ugly duckling had never seen anything so beautiful, and a strange cry came from his throat. So shrill it was that it frightened him, and he dived straight to the bottom of the pond. Up he came to swim round and round in dizzy circles. He would never forget the birds and he would love them always, more than anything else in the world, because they were so beautiful.

Winter set in, and the poor duckling swam as fast as he could to keep the water from freezing. But the hole grew smaller and smaller each day. At last, too tired to move, he was frozen fast in the ice.

That very morning a farmer chanced by, and breaking the ice with his shoe, carried the duckling home to his wife. The children were so happy they wanted to play with him. But the poor duckling was frightened, and straight into the milk pail he flew, and around the butter tub he whirled, and in and out of the meal barrel he fluttered.

The woman darted after him with the fire tongs, and the children laughed and shouted as they stumbled over each other, trying to catch him. Luckily the door was open, and out he flew into the bushes laden with snow. There he lay quite still, weary and sad, wondering what would happen to him next.

As the weeks and months went by, the poor duckling had a very bad time, indeed. But at last the springtime came again and the larks began to sing, and the little duckling was still alive in the reeds of the marsh.

Suddenly he began to flap his wings. Up, up into the air they carried him, far into the clear blue heavens. Then, as if by magic, he found himself in a beautiful garden with flowers blooming everywhere. Three graceful white swans drifted toward him slowly and a great sadness came over him.

"They will surely finish me, these beautiful creatures, because I am so ugly," he said to himself.

Rustling their feathers, they came nearer and nearer. "You may kill me now," cried the duckling, bending his head for them to strike.

But what was that, looking back at him from the water? It was no longer a dirty gray bird, big and heavy and clumsy. He was a beautiful white swan! Then what did it matter if he was born in a duckyard, if he had been hatched from a swan's egg?

Round and round him swam the three lovely swans, stroking him gently with their bills. The children in the garden ran to the water to throw him good bread and cake.

"See — a new swan!" they cried, running to bring their mother and father. "He is the handsomest of them all!"

The old swans bowed their heads to honor him and he was very happy. Suddenly he raised his head and rustling his snowy feathers, cried out for all to hear, "I never dreamed that such happiness could come to me, when I was a poor ugly duckling."

Into a new book of wonder tales went the story. But Hans was not a little worried as he sat working at his desk. All too little time there was, if the book was to be ready for Christmas. And how could there be Christmas without a new book of stories for the children?

For years now, "Uncle Hans" had not disappointed them. And the children in most of the lands around the world were not disappointed, either, with copies of the wonder tales printed in their own languages for them to enjoy.

Hans smiled as he thought of his last visit in England at the home of the great writer, Charles Dickens.

"Better not let the little ones know that you are here!" he had said. "They would keep you prisoner until every one of your tales had been dragged from you. Why, my dear Andersen, did you know that the English children will not go to sleep at night until they have had one of your stories?"

Faster scratched the pen at the beautiful desk. The Snow Queen? Ah yes, she must surely have her place between the covers of the new book. And all must be finished by late afternoon, when Hans would start out on a great adventure,—perhaps the very greatest of his lifetime. At the very thought, little chills began to run up and down his back.

"Ho, hum!" said he at last, putting down his pen and kicking off his red slippers. "Done, done, done. And time for Old Longlegs to be on his way to Odense."

Old Longlegs! Ah yes, the years were beginning to tell, with creaking in the joints and slower stride. Hans sighed as he took his place in the coach and jogged into the sunset. So much there was still to do for the children.

There would be bands to greet him when he arrived in Odense, and all of the townspeople, as well. Oh my, oh my! Hans shrank back onto the cushions at the thought of the great celebration waiting, the celebration to crown his long years.

But little did he know what was in store for him as he neared the end of his journey and found himself on the roadway leading into little Odense.

He sat up suddenly and blinked hard as they rolled into the

city. A sea of bright flags were flying over all the streets, and every house was decorated in his honor. Great banners waved in the sun, with HANS CHRISTIAN ANDERSEN shouting at him in bright letters. Never had he dreamed of anything like this!

He drew back in the corner and quickly pulled his hat down over his eyes. "No tears now, you silly fellow!" he scolded himself roundly. "You are coming home like a king, to honor and glory!"

A band of horsemen in bright red jackets and gleaming helmets, galloped out to meet him. Drawing their shining swords, they sat at attention while their leader gave his message of welcome.

"Hans Christian Andersen," said he, "The people of Odense await your coming with thanksgiving. This place of your birth, whose name you have made famous round the world, gives into your hands the Keys of the City. We salute this day the First Citizen of Odense."

A band struck up a stirring march and led the way through the streets, the horsemen guarding their precious visitor just behind.

"Andersen! Uncle Hans! Andersen!" Cheering throngs lined the gay streets and pushed on ahead, trying to keep up with the carriage.

Hans leaned from the window, waving and smiling. His eyes were on the children, and their high, clear voices were like music, calling out to him as they waved their tiny flags. "Uncle Hans! Uncle Hans! I'm here, Uncle Hans!"

"Oh, my pretty dears," he murmured, "no school today to celebrate your Uncle Hans. Just wait till you see the stories that he will write for you now!"

Banquets and speeches there were throughout the days for the beloved visitor and it was time, now, for the last biggest celebration of all.

Twilight deepened gently into night as Hans rode through the streets to the city square. He could not swallow the lump in his throat as every house window, glowing brightly with an Andersen Candle, lighted him on his way.

Bowing his great head, he murmured, "Thank you, God. You have been so kind to me, all of my long years."

Up to the balcony of the old City Hall he climbed, to find the big square below suddenly ablaze with flaming torches. Round and round in a giant circle marched hundreds of children, singing his own lovely hymn to Denmark.

As their clear, sweet voices came up to him, Hans could not stay his tears, and wept at the beauty of the shining faces beneath the torches.

The last pure tones swept on to the stars, and now from the center of the square a great bonfire was lighted. Higher and higher leaped the flames, and raising their torches to the heavens, the great crowd cheered again and again.

"Andersen! Andersen! Long live our Hans Christian Andersen!"

The beloved writer of fairy tales had indeed come home, a King.

THE END.